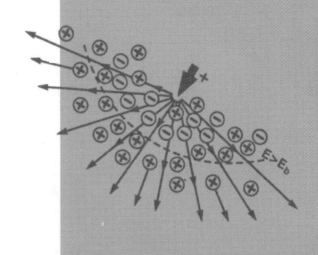

Electrostatics

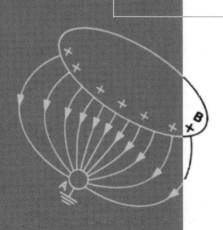

Join Us on the Internet

WWW: http://www.thomson.com
EMAIL: findit@kiosk.thomson.com

thomson.com is the on-line portal for the products, services and resources available from International Thomson Publishing (ITP).

This Internet kiosk gives users immediate access to more than 34 ITP publishers and over 20,000 products. Through *thomson.com* Internet users can search catalogs, examine subject-specific resource centers and subscribe to electronic discussion lists. You can purchase ITP products from your local bookseller, or directly through *thomson.com*.

Visit Chapman & Hall's Internet Resource Center for information on our new publications,
links to useful sites on the World Wide Web and an opportunity to join our e-mail mailing list.
Point your browser to: **http://www.chaphall.com** or
http://www.thomson.com/chaphall/electeng.html for Electrical Engineering

A service of

Electrostatics

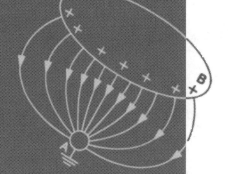

Niels Jonassen

Retired
Associate Professor
Department of Physics
Technical University
of Denmark

CHAPMAN & HALL

INTERNATIONAL THOMSON PUBLISHING
Thomson Science

New York • Albany • Bonn • Boston • Cincinnati
Detroit • London • Madrid • Melbourne
Mexico City • Pacific Grove • Paris • San Francisco
Singapore • Tokyo • Toronto • Washington

Cover design: Curtis Tow Graphics

Printed in the United States of America

Chapman & Hall
115 Fifth Avenue
New York, NY 10003

Chapman & Hall
2-6 Boundary Row
London SE1 8HN
England

Thomas Nelson Australia
102 Dodds Street
South Melbourne, 3205
Victoria, Australia

Chapman & Hall GmbH
Postfach 100 263
D-69442 Weinheim
Germany

International Thomson Editores
Campos Eliseos 385, Piso 7
Col. Polanco
11560 Mexico D.F
Mexico

International Thomson Publishing–Japan
Hirakawacho-cho Kyowa Building, 3F
1-2-1 Hirakawacho-cho
Chiyoda-ku, 102 Tokyo
Japan

International Thomson Publishing Asia
221 Henderson Road #05-10
Henderson Building
Singapore 0315

1 2 3 4 5 6 7 8 9 10 XXX 01 00 99 98

Library of Congress Cataloging-in-Publication Data

Jonassen, Niels, 1928-
    Electrostatics / Niels Jonassen.
        p.   cm.
    Includes index.
    ISBN 0-412-12861-6
    1. Electrostatics.   I. Title.
QC571.J65   1998
537.'2--DC21   96-29932
                                                      CIP

British Library Cataloguing in Publication Data available

"Electrostatics" is intended to present technically accurate and authoritative information from highly regarded sources. The publisher, editors, authors, advisors, and contributors have made every reasonable effort to ensure the accuracy of the information, but cannot assume responsibility for the accuracy of all information, or for the consequences of its use.

To order this or any other Chapman & Hall book, please contact **International Thomson Publishing, 7625 Empire Drive, Florence, KY 41042.** Phone: (606) 525-6600 or 1-800-842-3636. Fax: (606) 525-7778. e-mail: order@chaphall.com.

For a complete listing of Chapman & Hall titles, send your request to **Chapman & Hall, Dept. BC, 115 Fifth Avenue, New York, NY 10003.**

Contents

Preface

This book has developed from more than 40 years of work with static electric problems and almost as long a period of teaching courses on electrostatics, primarily at the Technical University of Denmark.

Several chapters of the book are hardly more than a brush-up of the general knowledge of most physicists 50 years ago. But with ever-increasing specialization, in today's teaching and research little attention seems to be paid to simple and basic relations. For this regrettable fact I am grateful.

It is my hope that the book may take the newcomer by the hand and also remind the specialist of some basic facts she may have forgotten or perhaps never learned.

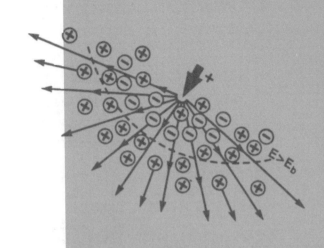

Electrostatics

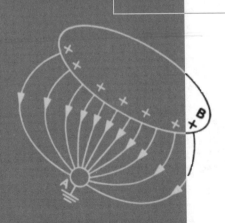

Chapter 1

Introduction

Static electricity may cause an unpleasant, but otherwise harmless shock, when you touch a door handle or kiss another person, after you have walked just a few steps on a dry, insulative carpet. Static electricity can also cause the slip (or shirt) to cling to your body, computers to go down, fibers to filter, or tankers to explode. But it is also by of static electric effects that we can clean the smoke from power plants, make photocopies or sandpaper, and separate iron ore and sand or rice and rodent excrements. Static electric processes have taken place on this planet as long as it has existed in its present form, with water vapor condensing to rain; with convective cloud systems developing huge electric dipoles, also known as thunderclouds, and with sand drifting across the desert.

Static electricity was, no doubt, the first type of electric process known to man. The first recorded mentioning of such phenomena is by Thales from Miletus, who as early as 600 B.C. stated that amber that had been rubbed was able to attract light objects such as hair, feathers, etc. And it is from this property of amber, in Greek *electron* (ελεκτρον), that we derive the words *electric* and *electricity*. But the actual knowledge of static electricity is much older. As A. D. Moore puts it in his book *Electrostatics*:

Did the cave man have a cat? If so he was our first electrical scientist ... he noticed the difference between unstroked fur and stroked fur.

More than 2000 years elapsed after the observation of Thales before the first systematic description of static electric phenomena appeared. This was the publishing of *De Magnete* by Gilbert in the year 1600, and over the next couple of centuries experimental work established a solid basis for an almost purely phenomenological knowledge of static electricity. At one extreme, new discoveries in electricity were used as party games in noble circles of society. But at the same time this developing science was explored by serious, although by modern standards rather primitive, scientists like Krüger and Kratzenstein in medicine and

1

experimental physics and simultaneously by more celebrated personalities like Coulomb, Dalibard, and Franklin. The latter two studied primarily the fascinating subsection of static electricity known as *atmospheric electricity*.

During the nineteenth century, however, batteries and generators for continuous electric currents were developed, and this markedly cooled the interest in electrostatics in favor of electrodynamics, with its obvious technical and general practical applicability. Around the beginning of the twentieth century a series of inventions was made based on electrostatic principles, prominent among these the electrofilter for removing particulates from air. But although these inventions gained a considerable and still-increasing use, the general knowledge of static electricity was very limited.

In education, electrostatics was for many years relegated to the introductory chapters of textbooks on electricity, the lectures occasionally spiced with slightly quaint demonstrations, involving the use of such items as chiming bells and rabbit fur. This situation began to change around the middle of the century with the appearance and increasingly widespread use of polymeric, highly insulative materials, and concepts from the world of electrostatics gradually became household words, mostly in connection with unwanted, harmful effects. When explosions in oil tankers and anaesthetic machines had to be explained, voltage and resistivity had to be reevaluated.

When photocopies were hard to handle and film negatives showed lightning images during the winter season, concepts like charges, electric fields, and brush discharges had to be considered. And when Mrs. Jones, Hansen, or Jönsson, living in modern well-insulated buildings, got electric shocks when touching the refrigerator or the husband, and also began to suffer from a series of diffuse, non-specific illnesses or maybe rather inconveniencies, like dry skin or mucosa, itching, stuffy breathing, migraine-type headaches, etc., people commonly described this as an effect of static electricity, normally without bothering to look for some kind of mechanism, not to mention other *possible* explanations. Static electricity became a kind of garbage can into which a lot of puzzling indoor climate problems could be conveniently placed. Of course the situation was immediately exploited by scientific frauds and witch doctors, who claimed they could solve the problem with their small, expensive, and useless boxes. Today, in the nineties, these same boxes, or some equally fraudulent gadgets, are marketed as remedies against present-day voodoo crazes, like *ground rays*.

But static electricity also began to make itself felt to an increasing degree in the electronic industry. Physicists and engineers gradually came to realize that the direct failure or latent breakdown of sensitive semiconductor components and circuits might be caused by an exposure to a static electric environment.

The static electric problems related to the electronic industry are probably of greater economic significance than those in any other branch of society. This may be the reason that this set of, scientifically speaking, rather simple problems even has its own name, *EOS* and *ESD*, or *electrical overstress* and *electrostatic discharge*. But even though a fund of specialized knowledge has been developed over the last decade, simple and basic static electric relations have often been handled in an impractical and sometimes erroneous way. Some electronics people, at least at the management level, seem to have been reasoning: "If voltage, current, and resistance are good enough to handle circuit problems, they are good enough to handle a little static!" As we shall see, it might be more practical to think in terms of fundamental quantities like *field strength, charge,* and *resistivity*.

Fortunately, over the last two decades, basic as well as applied research at many laboratories and companies around the world have not only established fundamental relations, but also developed means of fighting the risks and nuisances of static electricity. This has resulted in the appearance of several excellent, but admittedly rather specialized treatises on the topic. Nevertheless, there still seem to be numerous misconceptions and misunderstandings about static electricity.

It is the intention of this book to try to give a more general introduction to the whole field of electrostatics, with its harmful and bothersome effects as well as its many potential possibilities of use and application. We shall start by introducing the fundamental concepts and their physical, and unavoidably, mathematical relations. Some readers may find this introduction too formalistic and theoretical. They are advised to just skip the formulas. Others may find the definitions useful for reference.

Chapter 2

Fundamental Concepts

Both in everyday life and in more technical contexts one is often faced with phenomena or problems that can be meaningfully explained only if we assume the existence of a type of physical force different from the classical ones like gravity, friction, or elastic forces. This type of force is involved when photocopies stick together, when a television screen gets dirty, or when the expensive new hairdo is unmanageable. The type of force active in these cases is called an **electric force**, and we explain its presence by attributing a certain property to the materials or bodies on which the force is acting. This particular property is called the **electric charge**.

1. Electric Charge

Two bodies are said to have an electric charge, or just to be charged, if they interact with electric forces. The charge is a property of certain elementary particles, of which the most important are electrons and protons, both part of any atom of any material. The charge on a proton (the atomic nucleus of hydrogen) is called positive and written as e. The charge of an electron is correspondingly called negative and written $-e$. This indicates mathematically that the two charges are numerically equal and also that they can cancel each other's effect on a third charge. The designations, positive and negative, for electric charges were suggested by Benjamin Franklin.

The charge e $(-e)$ is called a positive (negative) elementary charge. It is the smallest existing amount of charge and would therefore appear to be an obvious choice as a unit of charge. In the **international system of units (systeme internationale, SI)**, however, the unit for charge, the **coulomb**, C, is a derived unit defined by

$$1 \text{ coulomb} = 1 \text{ ampere} \cdot \text{second},$$

which leads to

$$e = 1.602 \cdot 10^{-19} \, C$$

In a neutral atom or molecule the positive and negative charges are numerically equal; i.e., the number of protons in the atomic nucleus is equal to the number of electrons around the nucleus. If, however, some of the molecules in a body have an excess of electrons, the body is negatively charged; if there is a deficit, the body is positive. Experience has shown that charges of the same polarity repel and opposite polarities attract each other. All static electric charging processes involve electrons being transferred from one body or material to another.

Range of Charge

If a body loses or receives only one or a few electrons, the effect of the charge can only be detected if the body itself consists of a single atom or a few atoms. Such a charged atomic or molecular group is called an ion. If a charged particle of a powder is sticking to the wall of a container, the charge may be about 10^{-14} C, depending on the grain size, meaning that several hundred thousands of electrons have been exchanged.

If a person is charged to such a voltage that she may receive a shock by touching a water tap, her charge is at least 10^{-7} C; in other words, more than 10^{12} electrons have been exchanged in the charging. If a powder, like sugar or flour, is sliding down a tube, be it metal or plastic, the net charge on the powder is often about 10^{-7} C $\cdot$ kg^{-1}. If a plastic sheet is rubbed by a cloth, the charge separated is again often about 10^{-7} C.

There are, however, limits for the amount of charge that can be located on a surface. The maximum charge on a conductor at atmospheric pressure is about $3 \cdot 10^{-5}$ C $\cdot$ m^{-2}. We shall return to this problem when discussing electric fields.

2. Electric Field

An electric field is defined as a region where an electric charge experiences an electric force acting upon it. This is just another way of saying that the charge is in the neighborhood of, or in the field from, other charges. The force F on a charge q in an electric field is proportional to the charge itself, and can thus be written

$$F = q \cdot E \tag{2.1}$$

E is called the **electric field strength** and is determined by the magnitude and locations of the charges acting upon our charge q. It follows from equation (2.1) that a given field E will act in opposite directions upon positive and negative charges. The unit for field strength is [force/charge], i.e., **newton/coulomb**, N $\cdot$ C^{-1}. As we shall see later, this unit may also be given in **volt/meter**, V $\cdot$ m^{-1}.

The electric field from a given charge depends upon the distribution of and the distance from the charge. If a charge is located on a body with dimensions small compared to the distance to the points where the field strength is wanted, we talk about a **point charge**.

A point charge q (Figure 2.1) will at a point P at a distance r cause a field strength E given by

$$E = \frac{q}{4\pi\varepsilon_0 r^2}\,u \qquad\qquad (2.2)$$

where u is a unit vector in the direction from the charge towards P, and ε_0 is a fundamental constant, the **vacuum permittivity**, with the numerical value

$$\varepsilon_0 = 8.85(4187818)\cdot 10^{-12}\,\mathrm{C}^2\cdot\mathrm{N}^{-1}\cdot\mathrm{m}^{-2}$$

The unit for $\varepsilon_0{}^{*}$ can also be written as **farad/meter**, $\mathrm{F}\cdot\mathrm{m}^{-1}$, and the value is then

$$\varepsilon_0 = 8.85\cdot 10^{-12}\,\mathrm{F}\cdot\mathrm{m}^{-1} \qquad F = C^2/NM$$

The field from the charge q is plotted in Figure 2.2 a and b. The direction of the lines in Figure 2.2a is the direction of the field strength, and their density (through a plane perpendicular to the field strength) is proportional to the field strength. Such lines are called **field lines**. Figure 2.2b shows the variation of the field strength with the distance from the charge. As stated in equation (2.2), the field strength is inversely proportional to the square of the distance from the charge.

The field from any charge distribution can in principle be calculated from equation (2.1) by considering the distribution as made up of individual point charges and adding the field strengths from each of these charges. The field strengths to be added, however, are vectors varying in size and direction, and normally the summing, or rather integration, may at best be rather tedious. If, however, the charge distribution considered shows some degree of symmetry, the resulting field strength can often be easily calculated by use of the concept of **elec-**

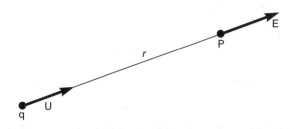

Figure 2.1 Field strength from positive point charge q

---

* The constant ε_0 is defined by $\varepsilon_0 = 1/(\mu_0 c)$ where μ_0 is the (magnetic) vacuum permeability and c is the vacuum speed of light.

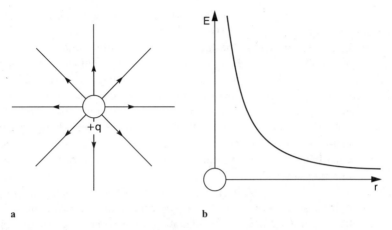

Figure 2.2 Field from positive point charge q: a. field lines, b. variation of field with distance

tric flux. The flux of an electric field E, also known as the E-flux, Φ_E, through a surface S is defined as

$$\Phi_E = \int_S E \cdot dS \qquad (2.3)$$

Here dS is an area segment of S, chosen so small that it can be considered as being a plane, and the field strength E is constant over dS. The vector dS is perpendicular to the area.

It can now be shown that if S is a closed surface in vacuum or air, equation (2.3) can be written

$$\int_{cs} E \cdot dS = \frac{q}{\varepsilon_0} \qquad (2.4)$$

Here q is the sum of all charges surrounded by the closed surface, independent of the distribution of the charges inside the surface. Equation (2.3) is called **Gauss' law** (or theorem) in integral form. Before demonstrating the use of Gauss' law it may be practical to give a basic review of the concept of conductors and insulators.

3. Conductors and Insulators

Equations (2.2) for the field strength from a point charge and (2.4) for the electric flux through a closed surface are both derived under the assumption that the fields extend themselves only in vacuum or air. If, however, an electric field is totally or just partly filled with some material, charges in the interior or on the surface of the material will experience forces from the field.

Some materials, known as **conductors**, contain mobile charge carriers in great numbers, and these carriers will then be moved by the field. The group of conductors comprises, most importantly, all metals, where the mobile charge carriers are **electrons**, and electrolytes, like most acids, bases, and salt solutions, in which the charge carriers are positive as well as negative **ions.** Other materials contain mobile charge carriers in such low numbers that an electric field only causes an insignificant or very weak transport of charge. Such materials are called **insulators**. As typical examples we find a series of polymeric materials like polyvinyl chloride (PVC), polystyrene, polytetrafluoroethylene (Teflon), polyethylene terephthalate (Mylar), polyamids (nylon), and many, many more, but also materials like rubber, porcelain, amber, mica, and quartz. The transition from conductors to insulators is, as we shall see, totally continuous.

If the field strength inside a material is calculated using the expressions valid for a vacuum, one must appreciate that the field, because of the charges in the atoms of the material, will vary strongly from point to point on an atomic scale. It appears, however, that a temporal and spatial mean value of the field, calculated on the basis of the vacuum formulas, gives a satisfactory macroscopic description of the fields inside the material.

If an electric charge is placed on a perfect insulator, the individual charges will repel each other, but this will not as a whole lead to a net transport of charge on or through the insulator, and the charges will stay where they were originally placed on the surface. This, however, is not the case when charges are placed on a conductor.

Let us consider an isolated conductor, A (Figure 2.3). When a charge q is placed on the conductor, the repulsion between the individual charges will make them move and distribute themselves until, almost momentarily, an equilibrium state is reached, where the resulting force on any charge is zero. When this state is established, *the field strength in the interior of the conductor is zero*. This means that the total net charge is located on the surface, because any excess charge in the interior of the conductor would create a net field that would cause a charge displacement, not complying with the assumed state of equilibrium. Further, the surface field strength must be perpendicular to the surface, because any tangential component would again cause a charge displacement.

If the conductor is placed far away from other conductors, the distribution of charges on the surface will be determined solely by the shape and size of the conductor, in such a way that the charges will be located most densely around points and sharp edges of the conductor, and these will therefore also be the places of highest surface field strengths, as indicated in Figure 2.3.

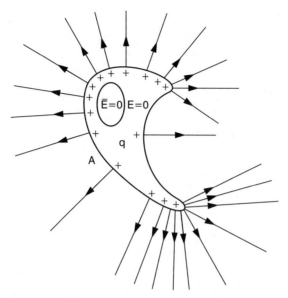

Figure 2.3 Charge distribution on isolated conductor

4. Electrostatic Induction

In Figure 2.4a is shown a positively charged insulator *A*. If an uncharged, isolated conductor *B* is placed in the field from *A*, some of the electrons in *B* will move in the field, in this case toward *A*, causing *B* to develop a negative charge on the one side and a positive charge on the opposite side where there is a deficit of electrons. This phenomenon is called **electrostatic induction**, and the charges on *B* are called induced charges. In loose terms the process can be described as some of the field lines from the charge *q* on *A* ending on the negative charge on *B* and an equally large number originating from the induced positive charge on *B*. The electric field shown in Figure 2.4 can be considered as the sum of two fields, the original field from *A*, because the charge distribution on *A* is unaffected by the presence of *B* (*A* is an insulator), and the field from the positive and negative induced charges on *B*.

If the conductor *B* is connected to ground, Figure 2.4b, electrons from the ground will flow to *B* to make up the deficit of electrons on the right side of *B*, or more correctly, the deficit of electrons in *B* will distribute itself on *B* and the ground as a whole and thus be so small at any point that there is no essential effect. When the conductor B is grounded, the induced positive charge on the right side of *B* is able to leak away, and this charge is therefore called the **free induced charge**. The negative induced charge on the left side of *B*, on the other hand, is bound by the field and called the **bound induced charge**. When the free

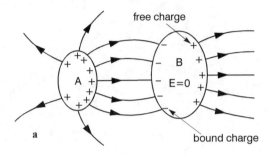

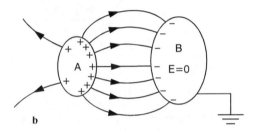

Figure 2.4 Induction

charge disappears, the distribution and magnitude of the bound charge will also change in such a way that the field strength inside *B* is still zero, and at the surface perpendicular to the surface.

If the ground connection is broken and *B* is removed from the field from *A*, the former bound negative charge is now free to move and will distribute itself in such a way that the field conditions for a conductor are again fulfilled. The conductor *B* has thus been charged by induction. The presence of the uncharged conductor *B* in the field from *A* will change, or deform, this field, but will not affect the charge distribution on (the insulator) *A*. If, on the other hand, *A* is a *charged conductor*, the introduction of another (uncharged) conductor in its field will change not only the field but also the charge distribution on the original conductor in a rather complicated way, causing the charge on *A* to be concentrated on the side facing *B*.

5. Polarization

If the uncharged body *B* in Figure 2.4 is an insulator, charge displacement, or induction, as in a conductor is not possible, because the supply of mobile charge carriers is negligible. Another process, however, called **polarization**, takes place. Polarization involves the interaction between an external field and dipoles in the material. An **electric dipole** consists of two equal charges of opposite polarity at a fixed distance. When a material is being polarized, either electric dipoles will be formed, for instance by a slight deformation of the usually symmetrical, atomic electron clouds, or already existing molecular dipoles, normally randomly distributed, will be partly aligned by the external field.

Although the basic polarization process is always the same, in practice the effects of polarization appear in two completely different ways. If small, light particles, like airborne dust, are exposed to an electric field, the particles will be polarized and moved in the direction of convergence of the field. This is why dust is attracted to the television screen or to wafers that are not properly neutralized by ionized air. This is also (partly) the effect being utilized in the electrostatic manufacture of sandpaper and in the flocking process.

If the field from a given charge distribution (i.e., **for constant charge**) is being filled, totally or in part, by a polarizable material, called a **dielectric**, the field at a point inside the dielectric will normally be reduced by a factor ε_r, called the relative permittivity of the material. This relation is the basis for the use of dielectrics in capacitors for increasing the capacitance. Both properties and applications of the polarization process will be discussed in detail in Chapter 8.

6. More About Electric Fields: Application of Gauss' Law

It has already been mentioned that the electric field from a symmetric charge distribution, even if extensive, may be conveniently described and calculated by the use of Gauss' law

$$\int_{cs} \boldsymbol{E} \cdot d\boldsymbol{S} = \frac{q}{\varepsilon_0}$$

which states that *the surface integral over any closed surface of the normal component of the electric field equals the enclosed charge divided by the vacuum permittivity*. We shall show a few examples of the application of this rule.

Field from Uniformly Charged Sphere

In Figure 2.5 is shown a sphere of radius R. A charge q is uniformly distributed on the surface of the sphere. For a conducting sphere this condition is always fulfilled as long as the sphere is far removed from any other objects.

At a point P at a distance r from the center O of the sphere we have a field strength E, the magnitude of which can only depend on r and q, and which for reasons of symmetry must point in the direction of r.

We now place an (imaginary) spherical surface S with a radius r ($> R$) concentric with the charged sphere. Because the field strength E at any point will be directed along r, we find that

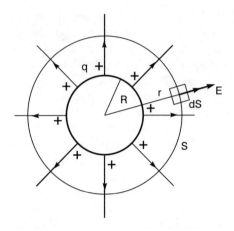

Figure 2.5 Field from charged sphere

$$\int_S \boldsymbol{E} \cdot d\boldsymbol{S} = E4\pi r^2 = \frac{q}{\varepsilon_0}$$

or

$$E = \frac{q}{4\pi\varepsilon_0 r^2} \quad \text{for } r > R \tag{2.5}$$

Equation (2.5) indicates that the field at any point outside the charged sphere is the same as if the charge had been located at the center of the sphere.

If, on the other hand, the surface S had been drawn with a radius $r < R$, i.e., inside the charged sphere, the symmetry conditions would still be fulfilled, but now the enclosed charge and hence the field strength at any point would be zero, i.e.,

$$E = 0 \quad \text{for } r < R \tag{2.6}$$

EXAMPLE 2.1:

A charge $q = 10^{-8}$ C is distributed uniformly on the surface of a sphere of radius $R = 0.1$ m. The surface charge density is $\sigma = 8 \cdot 10^{-8}$ C $\cdot$ m^{-2}. At a distance $r = 1$ m from the center of the sphere the field strength is, according to equation (2.5),

$$E = \frac{10^{-8}}{4\pi\varepsilon_0 \cdot 1^2} = 90\,\text{V} \cdot \text{m}^{-1}$$

At a distance $r = 10$ m the field strength is

$$E \approx 0.9\,\text{V} \cdot \text{m}^{-1}$$

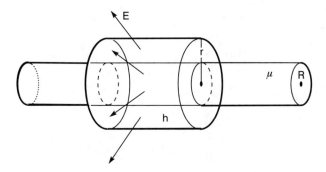

Figure 2.6 Field from charged cylinder

Field from Cylindrical Charge Distribution

In Figure 2.6 is shown a (long) cylinder of radius R. The cylinder is uniformly charged on the curved surface with a linear charge density μ $(C \cdot m^{-1})$.

In order to determine the electric field from the charge distribution we consider a cylindrical surface S of radius r and length h with its axis coinciding with the axis of the charged cylinder. For reasons of symmetry the field strength will only depend on q and r and be perpendicular to the curved surfaces. The E-flux through the plane end surfaces of S is therefore zero, and equation (2.4) yields

$$\int_S E \cdot dS = E2\pi rh = \frac{\mu h}{\varepsilon_0}$$

or

$$E = \frac{\mu}{2\pi\varepsilon_0 r} \quad \text{for } r \geqslant R \tag{2.7}$$

and, as for the charged sphere,

$$E = 0 \quad \text{for } r < R \tag{2.8}$$

EXAMPLE 2.2:

A cylinder of radius $R = 0.1$ m is uniformly charged with the linear charge density $\mu = 5 \cdot 10^{-8} C \cdot m^{-1}$, corresponding to a surface charge density $\sigma \approx 8 \cdot 10^{-8}$ $C \cdot m^{-2}$. At a distance $r = 1$ m from the axis of the cylinder the field strength is, according to equation (2.7),

$$E = \frac{5 \cdot 10^{-8}}{2\pi\varepsilon_0 \cdot 1} \approx 900 \, V \cdot m^{-1}$$

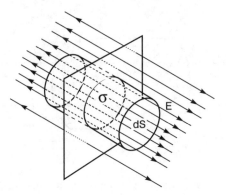

Figure 2.7 Field from charged plane

At a distance $r = 10$ m the field strength is

$$E \approx 90 \text{ V} \cdot \text{m}^{-1}$$

Field from Uniformly Charged Plane

In Figure 2.7 is shown a section of an infinitely large plane surface uniformly charged with a positive charge of density σ (C $\cdot$ m^{-2}).

The closest realization of this situation is a uniformly charged sheet of plastic. For reasons of symmetry the field strength must have the same value on both sides of the surface and be perpendicular to the surface.

We now consider a small cylindrical surface placed around the charged surface in such a way that the axis of the cylinder is perpendicular to the surface and the ends of the cylinder, each with an area dS, are placed on either side of and parallel to the charged surface. The cylinder will thus enclose a charge σdS and as there is no flux through the curved surface, equation (2.4) will give

$$EdS + EdS = \frac{\sigma dS}{\varepsilon_0}$$

or

$$E = \frac{\sigma}{2\varepsilon_0} \tag{2.9}$$

We see that the field strength is independent of the distance from the plane charge. It should be stressed that this is only true as long as the linear dimensions of the charged surface are large compared to the distance to the point where the field is considered.

EXAMPLE 2.3:

An infinitely large plane is uniformly charged with a surface charge density $\sigma = 8 \cdot 10^{-8}$ C $\cdot$ m^{-2}. The field strength in front of the plane is, according to equation (2.9),

$$E = \frac{8 \cdot 10^{-8}}{2\varepsilon_0} \simeq 4500\,\text{V} \cdot \text{m}^{-1}$$

Field in Front of Charged Conductor

Let us consider a plane section of a charged conductor with surface charge density σ (see Figure 2.8). As mentioned earlier, the field strength will be perpendicular to the surface of a conductor and zero inside.

We now place a cylindrical surface in the same way as in the previous example and find from equation (2.4)

$$EdS = \frac{\sigma dS}{\varepsilon_0}$$

and

$$E = \frac{\sigma}{\varepsilon_0} \qquad\qquad (2.10)$$

EXAMPLE 2.4:

A plane conductor is charged with a charge density $\sigma = 8 \cdot 10^{-8}$ C $\cdot$ m^{-2}. The field in front of the conductor is, according to equation (2.10),

$$E = \frac{8 \cdot 10^{-8}}{\varepsilon_0} = 9000\,\text{V} \cdot \text{m}^{-1}$$

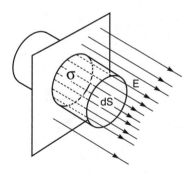

Figure 2.8 Field in front of charged conductor

Although it is often assumed that the field strength decreases inversely proportional to the square of the distance to the charge creating the field, as is shown from the preceding examples, this is often not the case.

Field in Cavities of Conductor, Faraday Screen

Without going into the mathematical derivation, we will state that the field inside a hollow conductor is always zero if no charges are present in the cavity. This is true regardless of the shape of the conductor and the cavity and also of whether or not the conductor as a whole is charged. When a conducting enclosure of this type is used to screen off the fields from outside charges, it is called a **Faraday screen** (or cage, pail, etc.). The field-screening effect of a conducting enclosure for the protection of sensitive semiconductor components will be discussed later.

7. Electrical Potential, Voltage

The effect of a given charge distribution can always be described if the field strength is known at every point of the environment of the charges. It is, however, often convenient and sufficient to express an integral effect in a given point of the field as a single (scalar) figure, called the **potential** or **voltage**.

If a charge Q is placed in an electric field E (see Figure 2.9), the field force F on Q is, according to equation (2.1),

$$F = QE$$

If the charge Q is moved from a point A to a point B, the work done by the field will be

$$W_{AB} = Q \int_A^B E \cdot da \qquad (2.11)$$

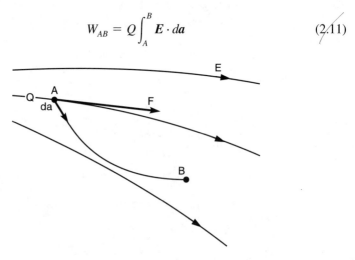

Figure 2.9 Work on charge in electric field

It can be shown that this work is independent of the route from A to B and only depends on the start and finish points A and B. Mathematically speaking, this means that the electric field is **conservative**. Equation (2.11) can thus be written

$$W_{AB} = Q\,[V_A - V_B] \qquad (2.12)$$

where

$$V_A - V_B = \int_A^B E \cdot da \qquad (2.13)$$

The quantity $V_A - V_B$ is called the **potential difference** or **voltage difference** between the points A and B and we thus have the following definition: *The potential difference between the points A and B in an electric field is equal to the (line) integral of the electric field strength from A to B.* It appears from equation (2.12) that the unit for potential difference, [work/charge], is **joule/coulomb** which is called **volt** (V), i.e.,

$$1\ \text{V} = 1\ \text{J} \cdot \text{C}^{-1}$$

Because $1\ \text{J} = 1\ \text{N} \cdot \text{m}$ we see that the unit for field strength, $\text{N} \cdot \text{C}^{-1}$, may also be expressed as $\text{V} \cdot \text{m}^{-1}$.

Equation (2.13) only defines **potential differences**, and in principle any point in a field can be chosen as the point of zero potential. Often the potential is chosen to be zero at an **infinitely far point**, which is defined as any point so far away from the charge distribution producing the field that the field strength is infinitesimally small (≈ 0). The integral of the field strength between all such points is zero, thus from equation (2.13) they all have the same potential, and it is practical to let this common potential be zero. The **potential V** at a point P of an electric field is thus defined as

$$V = \int_P^\infty E \cdot da \qquad (2.14)$$

The ground can be considered a conductor and the field strength in its interior is therefore (normally) equal to zero. Consequently, all points on and in the ground have, according to equation (2.13), the same potential. Because any infinitely far point, and thus also any infinitely far point in the ground, has zero potential, the ground as a whole can be considered a region of zero potential.

Although the potential is a property of any point in an electric field, in everyday practical use the concept of potential is normally connected with charged surfaces or bodies (unfortunately, often in a rather misunderstood and even erroneous way).

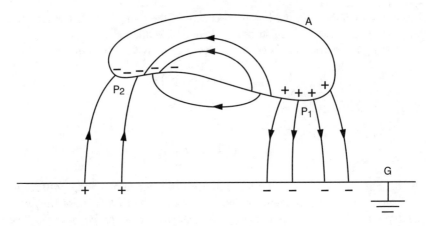

Figure 2.10 Surface potential of charged insulator

state of being neat?

Surface Potential of Insulator

Let us consider a positively charged insulator A (Figure 2.10) in the vicinity of a grounded plane G.

The charge will create a field between A and G where the field strength in a given point depends upon the geometry *and* upon the distribution of the charge on A. The integral of the field strength from, say point P_1, to G

$$V_{P_1} = \int_{P_1}^{G} \mathbf{E} \cdot d\mathbf{a}$$

is, according to equation (2.13), the (surface) potential of the point P_1 on the surface of the insulator, and may in the example shown be, say +500 V. If the integral is taken from another point, say P_2 on A, the value and thus the potential will usually be different, in this case maybe -90 V. The surface potential of an insulator can thus vary from point to point and will, at a given point, depend upon not only the charge at the point in question but also upon the distribution of charges over the remainder of the insulator.

Only in the case where we have a plane, uniformly charged insulator placed parallel to a grounded plane (see Figure 2.11) will the surface potential adequately describe the electrical state of the charged body. If the surface charge density is σ and if the distance d to ground is small compared to the dimensions of the charged plane, from equation (2.4) the field strength in the space between the plane and ground is

$$E = \frac{\sigma}{\varepsilon_0}$$

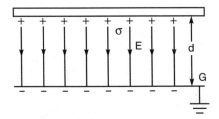

Figure 2.11 Surface potential of uniformly charged plate

According to (2.13), the potential of the uniformly charged plate will thus be

$$V = Ed = \frac{\sigma}{\varepsilon_0} d$$

A measurement of the surface density and the distance might thus lead to the surface potential and hence to a description of the electrical state of the charged plane. This, however, is the only way in which the surface potential can be determined. *Surface potentials can not be measured.* And the situation in Figure 2.11 is the only one in which the surface potential gives an adequate characterization of the state of charge, and then only if the distance d is kept constant. Consequently, the use of the concept surface potential should be limited to such situations, for instance when dealing with **electrets**, of which we will hear more later on. In all other cases of charged insulators the surface density and the field from the charge are far more relevant parameters for describing the effects of the charges, and these quantities can actually be measured.

 Why then does the concept of surface potential nevertheless appear frequently in accounts of static electric phenomena or even in lists of material properties? The explanation is probably that most people have been brought up thinking of electricity in terms of circuits, current, resistance, and voltage. But the voltage is always the voltage of *conductors*. If by some kind of mental inertia one tries to explain noncircuit problems using circuit-related concepts, the result is confusion and misunderstanding. But potential or voltage is a very useful and handy concept when used properly, i.e., in connection with insulated charged conductors, as we shall see in the next section.

Potential of Conductor, Capacitance

Let us consider a positively charged insulated conductor A (Figure 2.12) in the vicinity of a grounded plane G. The charge q will distribute itself on the surface of A in such a way that (a) the field strength inside the conductor is zero at any point and (b) the field strength at the surface is perpendicular to the surface.

 According to (2.13) the potential difference between any two points in or on A is thus zero, or any point P in or on the conductor has the same potential

electrets: a dielectric body in which a permanent state of electric polarization has been set up

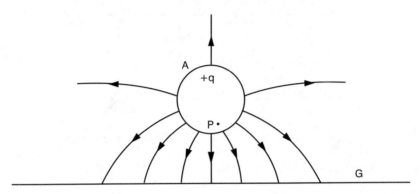

Figure 2.12 Potential of charged conductor

$$V_P = \int_P^G E \cdot da \qquad (2.15)$$

V_P (or just V) is therefore called the **potential** of the conductor. If the charge q is changed, the field around A will change but will keep the same form, i.e., at any point around A be proportional to q. Hence the potential V of A will also be proportional to q as long as the geometry is kept constant. This relationship is normally written

$$q = CV \qquad (2.16)$$

The factor C is called the **capacitance** of A relative to ground. The capacitance is a geometrical quantity, depending upon the dimensions and shape as well as the placing of the conductor A relative to the ground G. The unit for capacitance is charge/voltage, i.e., **coulomb/volt**, and is called the **farad**, F, so

$$1\,F = 1\,C \cdot V^{-1}$$

A capacitance of 1 F is an extremely large capacitance, so normally subunits are used. In circuits these are usually μF and nF, whereas in static electric contexts the subunit of pF $= 10^{-12}$ F suffices.

It should be stressed that the concept of capacitance has meaning only in connection with insulated conductors. The capacitance of a conductor or a system of conductors determines the voltage to which a given charge can raise the conductor and also the energy that is stored in the system for a given charge. It is therefore important to be able to measure, calculate, or estimate the magnitude of the capacitance of commonly encountered systems. For systems of simple geometry, equation (2.4) yields the field between the conductor and ground for a given charge, equation (2.15) gives the corresponding voltage, and equation (2.16) gives the capacitance. In the following section an example of this procedure will be given.

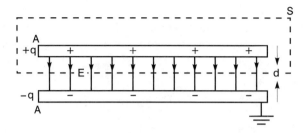

Figure 2.13 Parallel plate capacitor

Parallel Plate Capacitor

The simplest capacitive system is the **parallel plate capacitor**, consisting of two normally plane plates (see Figure 2.13).

The area of the plates is A and the distance between the plates is d. We ground one of the plates and give the other a charge q. By induction a charge of opposite polarity of q will be bound on the grounded plate. When d is small compared to the dimensions of the plates, this charge will practically be equal to $-q$. Almost the whole charge is located on the sides of the plates facing each other, and the electric field will be homogeneous in the region between the plates and zero outside this region. If a closed surface S is placed as shown in Figure 2.13, equation (2.4) yields

$$\int_S \boldsymbol{E} \cdot d\boldsymbol{S} = EA = \frac{q}{\varepsilon_0}$$

$$E = \frac{q}{A\varepsilon_0} \tag{2.17}$$

According to (2.15) the potential difference between the plates is

$$V = Ed = \frac{q}{A\varepsilon_0} d \tag{2.18}$$

and from (2.16) we then find the capacitance

$$C = \varepsilon_0 \frac{A}{d} \tag{2.19}$$

Equation (2.19) assumes that we have a vacuum between the capacitor plates. But this formula can also be used with very good approximation when the space between the plates is filled with air or other gases. If, however, the space between the capacitor plates is filled with an insulator, or dielectric, like polystyrene, the field strength in the capacitor is for a given charge a factor ε_r times smaller, and consequently the capacitance is ε_r times greater. The quantity ε_r is called the **relative permittivity** or **dielectric constant** of the insulator. We thus have the following general expression for the **capacitance of a parallel plate capacitor**:

$$C = \varepsilon_r \varepsilon_0 \frac{A}{d} \qquad (2.20)$$

EXAMPLE 2.5:

The plates in a parallel plate capacitor have area $A = 100 \text{ cm}^2$ separated by a distance $d = 1.00$ mm. The space between the plates is filled by a dielectric of relative permittivity $\varepsilon_r = 4$. According to equation (2.20) the capacitance is

$$C = 4 \cdot 8.85 \cdot 10^{-12} \cdot \frac{100 \cdot 10^{-4}}{1 \cdot 10^{-3}} = 354 \text{ pF}$$

Although equation (2.20) is derived for the system shown in Figure 2.13, it may be used for estimating the capacitance of other less well-defined systems, for instance, the capacitance of a standing person, insulated from ground by the floor covering and her footwear (see Figure 2.14).

When an insulated person is charged, the charge will distribute itself in such a way that all points on the person have the same voltage with respect to ground, as explained in the section Potential of Conductor, Capacitance. This implies that the charge will be densely located on areas close to the ground. For

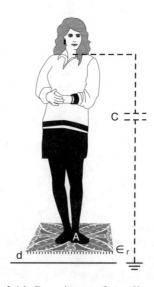

Figure 2.14 Capacitance of standing person

a standing person who is not actually leaning against a wall, the shortest distance is through the soles and the floor covering. Consequently, most of the charge will be located on the soles of the feet and by induction bind an equally large, opposite charge in a (conducting) layer of the floor, very much as shown in Figure 2.13.

The capacitance can thus be calculated from equation (2.20), with an area A equal to the area of the soles, about 300 cm^2, the distance d equal to the (effective) thickness of the soles plus the insulating floor covering, about 5–10 mm, and an ε_r of about 4–10. This leads to a capacitance in the range of 100–300 pF. If the parameters A, d, and ε_r are actually determined for a given person, and if her capacitance is also measured directly, the value estimated from equation (2.20) will normally be about 60–70 % of the measured value, indicating that this fraction of the total charge is on the feet.

8. Dielectrics, D-Fields

As mentioned earlier, the electric field from a given charge distribution may be modified by the presence of insulators or dielectrics, because of polarization, i.e., the field-induced formation of electric dipoles in the dielectric. In other words, the electric field is not determined solely by the magnitude of the charges but also by the electric properties of the region of the field. The formulas derived so far can, however, also be used in dielectric media (when the necessary symmetry conditions prevail) if the vacuum permittivity is replaced by the constant

$$\varepsilon = \varepsilon_r \varepsilon_0 \tag{2.21}$$

which is called the **absolute permittivity** of the material. The relative permittivity ε_r, already introduced in connection with the use of dielectrics in capacitors, is a measure of the ability of the dielectric to be polarized. Gauss' law, equation (2.4), will thus in a dielectric be

$$\int_{cs} E \cdot dS = \frac{q}{\varepsilon} \tag{2.22}$$

It now appears to be useful to introduce, in addition to the electric field E, an extra field quantity, D, called the **electric field density**, the **dielectric displacement**, or just the D-field. The dielectric displacement is defined in terms of the electric field E and the degree of polarization in the medium, caused by E. For electrical isotropic materials D is proportional to E and can be written

$$D = \varepsilon E \tag{2.23}$$

The unit for D is charge/area, i.e., **coulomb**/m^2 (C $\cdot$ m^{-2}). By introducing equation (2.23) in the formulas already derived for the E-field from various charge distributions, we see that the D-field will follow the E-field, but will be independent of the material. As an example, the D-field from a point charge will be

$$D = \frac{q}{4\pi r^2} u \qquad (2.24)$$

corresponding to the E-field, given by equation (2.2). **Gauss' law for the D-field** will be

$$\int_{cs} D \cdot dS = q \qquad (2.25)$$

where q is the charge surrounded by the closed surface.

9. Electric Fields in Air and Dielectrics

Electrical breakdown (Air)

Under normal circumstances atmospheric air is considered a good insulator, and a charged insulated or insulating body will loose its charge slowly when surrounded by air. The reason for this is that air, as a rule, contains very few charged particles, or ions, which by being attracted to the charged body might neutralize its charge. The "natural" air ions are formed primarily by radioactive (and to a lesser extent cosmic) radiation.

Ionization causes an electron to be knocked off an air molecule, oxygen or nitrogen, leaving the molecule as a singly, positively charged **elementary ion**, which within a fraction of a second will attract 10–15 molecules (mostly water) forming a molecular cluster called a **positive air ion**. The electron will almost immediately attach to (normally) an uncharged oxygen molecule and thus form a negative elementary ion. The negative elementary ion will also attract maybe 8–12 water molecules to form a **negative air ion**. This ionization process will under normal circumstances only create a small number of ion pairs (about 5–10 ion pairs per cm^3 per s), but the production rate will increase very markedly if the electric field strength in the air exceeds a critical value, the **breakdown field strength**, E_b, which at atmospheric pressure has the approximate value

$$E_b \approx 3 \cdot 10^6 \text{ V} \cdot \text{m}^{-1} \qquad (2.26)$$

As explained above, an electron is knocked off a neutral molecule by natural ionization, and if this happens in an electrical field, the electron will move and be accelerated in the field. If the accelerating field strength exceeds E_b, the electron may, before it collides with a molecule, gain a kinetic energy sufficiently large ($\approx 5.5 \cdot 10^{-18}$ J or 34 eV) to enable it to ionize the molecule, i.e., to free an electron, which may in turn be accelerated to ionization, and so on. This process is called **ionization by collision**. The process will take place in the whole region where the field strength exceeds E_b and will give rise to an **electrical discharge**, i.e., a transport of charge by the ions being moved by the field. If the breakdown field strength is exceeded along some path, i.e., ions are formed all along the path from a charged conductor to ground (or to a conductor at a different potential), the result is a **breakdown.**

According to equation (2.10), the field in front of a charged conductor with surface density σ is

$$E = \frac{\sigma}{\varepsilon_0}$$

Consequently, the **maximum surface charge density** σ_m on a conductor (in air at atmospheric pressure) is

$$\sigma_m = \varepsilon_0 E_b \simeq 2.7 \cdot 10^{-5}\, C \cdot m^{-2} \qquad (2.27)$$

The breakdown field strength value from equation (2.26) holds for plane electrodes. At points (and wires) the field strength has to be higher before ionization sets in. On the other hand, the charge will, as mentioned earlier, be densely located around points and protrusions on a conductor, and according to equation (2.10), the field strength will be especially high in such areas, which will counterbalance the fact that the breakdown field strength is higher. As a result a discharge from a conductor will normally start from points or edges.

Dielectric Ionization

In dielectrics ionization may also occur when the field strength exceeds a certain value, characteristic for the material in question. The process of ionization is somewhat similar to that in air. However, one difference is that a dielectric in which breakdown has occurred normally is ruined, whereas the air almost momentarily will regain its initial insulating properties. Normally the breakdown field strength of dielectrics is considerably higher than that of air.

Table 2.1 shows the breakdown field strength and relative permittivity for some commonly used materials.

Breakdown Voltage

As explained above, it is the electrical field strength that determines whether or not a discharge or flashover will take place in a given material. When the breakdown field strengths for the materials used are known, it is thus possible to calculate the maximum voltage differences that can be maintained in a given setup, before a discharge sets in.

Table 2.1 Breakdown field strength and relative
permittivity of commonly used materials

Material	E_b $(\mathrm{V} \cdot \mathrm{m}^{-1})$	ϵ_r
Air	$3.0 \cdot 10^6$	1.000536
Mica	$1.0 \cdot 10^8$	5.4
Mylar	$1.5 \cdot 10^8$	3.0
Plexiglass	$4.0 \cdot 10^7$	3.4
Polystyrene	$2.4 \cdot 10^7$	2.5
Porcelain	$6.0 \cdot 10^6$	7.0
Teflon	$1.0 \cdot 10^7$	2.1
Barium titanate	$5.0 \cdot 10^6$	1200

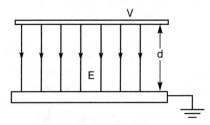

Figure 2.15 Voltage and field strength in a single material

Let us consider a simple example. Two parallel plates are placed a distance d from each other (see Figure 2.15). If the breakdown field strength for the material between the plates is E_b, the maximum voltage difference, or breakdown voltage, V_b, that can be maintained between the plates is

$$V_b = E_b d \tag{2.28}$$

EXAMPLE 2.6:

With $d = 0.1$ m (Figure 2.15) and air between the plates the maximum voltage is

$$V_{b,a} = 3 \cdot 10^6 \cdot 0.1 = 3 \cdot 10^5 \text{ V}$$

With plexiglass between the plates the maximum voltage is

$$V_{b,p} = 4 \cdot 10^7 \cdot 0.1 = 4 \cdot 10^6 \text{ V}$$

Equation (2.28) is valid only when the entire volume between the plates is filled with the same material.

In Figure 2.16 are again shown two parallel plates separated by a distance d. The interspace is filled by two dielectrics of relative permittivities ε_1 and ε_2, breakdown field strengths E_{b1} and E_{b2}, and thicknesses a and b, where

$$d = a + b$$

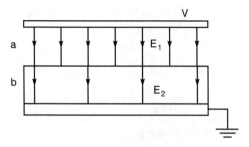

Figure 2.16 Voltage and field strengths in two dielectrics

If the field strengths in the two materials are E_1 and E_2, respectively, the voltage difference between the plates is given by

$$V = E_1 a + E_2 b \qquad (2.29)$$

If the surface charge density on the plates is σ, we have, according to equations (2.10) and (2.21),

$$E_1 = \frac{\sigma}{\varepsilon_1 \varepsilon_0} \quad \text{and} \quad E_2 = \frac{\sigma}{\varepsilon_2 \varepsilon_0}$$

$$\text{or} \quad E_2 = \frac{\varepsilon_1}{\varepsilon_2} E_1 \qquad (2.30)$$

Equation (2.29) can thus be written

$$V = E_1 a + \frac{\varepsilon_1}{\varepsilon_2} E_1 b \qquad (2.31)$$

Because E_1 has to be $< E_{b1}$ and $E_2 < E_{b2}$, the maximum voltage between the plates is determined by E_{b1}, if $E_{b2} > \varepsilon_1/\varepsilon_2 E_{b2}$. In this case we have

$$V_b = E_{b1} a + \frac{\varepsilon_1}{\varepsilon_2} E_{b1} b \qquad (2.32)$$

EXAMPLE 2.7:

Let material 1 (see Figure 2.16) be air and material 2 be plexiglass, and let $a = b = 0.05$ m. The maximum voltage between the plates is then, according to equation (2.32),

$$V_b = 3 \cdot 10^6 \cdot 0.05 + \frac{1}{3.4} \cdot 3 \cdot 10^6 \cdot 0.05 = \text{ca.} \; 2 \cdot 10^5 \; V$$

Comparing Examples 2.6 and 2.7, we find that when a dielectric in the region between two plates is partly replaced by a dielectric with a higher permittivity, the maximum voltage between the plates will be lower, even if the new dielectric has a higher breakdown field strength.

10. Types of Discharges

As we have explained, ionization will take place and charges will be moved if the field strength at a given point exceeds a critical value, the breakdown field strength, characteristic for the material in question. The course of the resulting discharge, however, depends strongly, among other factors, upon the geometry of the body where the discharge starts and the nature of the material through which it develops.

Corona Discharge

If a conducting electrode in the shape of a sharp point (or a thin wire) is held at a sufficiently high potential, maybe 2–20 kV, the breakdown field strength may be exceeded in a region of a few millimeters around the electrode (see Figure 2.17).

In this region positive and negative ions will be formed, as explained above, and ions of opposite polarity to the electrode voltage will be attracted towards the electrode, where they will be neutralized. Ions of the same polarity as that of the electrode will be repelled and, once outside the ionization region will move away towards grounded surroundings with velocities rapidly decreasing with the distance from the electrode from about $100 \text{ m} \cdot \text{s}^{-1}$ to maybe $1\text{--}2 \text{ cm} \cdot \text{s}^{-1}$.

This kind of discharge is called a **corona** or **silent** discharge. In the dark, a bluish luminescence may be seen in the region of ionization. Characteristic features of a corona discharge are the extreme limited region of ionization and the low energy density, which makes it impossible to ignite even the most flammable gas mixture by a corona discharge.

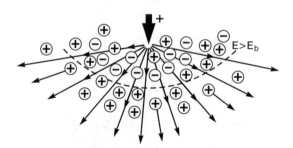

Figure 2.17 Corona discharge

Spark Discharge

The best-known type of electric discharge is the **spark**. Although the name is commonly used for almost any kind of charge transfer through dielectrics (including air), it ought to be reserved for the discharge between two conductors (without sharp protrusions) at different potentials.

In a spark, ionization takes place along and the charge is transferred through a narrow channel between the two conductors. In this channel most of the energy stored in the field between the conductors will be dissipated. If the (partial) capacitance of the two conductors is C and their potential difference is V, the energy W dissipated in the discharge is given by

$$W = \frac{1}{2} CV^2 \tag{2.33}$$

Because the discharge channel is very narrow and short and the discharge as a whole very fast, the energy density of a spark discharge can be very high, making the spark discharge the most incendive of all types of discharges.

Brush Discharge

If a discharge takes place between a small electrode (radius of curvature in the order of millimeters) and ground, the discharge may be a **brush discharge**, characterized by moving irregular luminescent discharge paths. The energy density in a brush discharge is higher than in a corona discharge and may be high enough to ignite certain vapor mixtures.

Discharges from Insulators

It should be mentioned that discharges may also take place to or from charged insulators. Such discharges will always be corona or brush discharges. We shall discuss this phenomenon when dealing with the effects of static electricity.

11. Mobility

If an electric field is established in a material containing mobile charge carriers, the positive charges will flow in the direction of the field, and the negative charges will flow in the opposite direction. The force F on a carrier with the charge q exposed to a field of strength E is

$$F = qE$$

and, from Newton's second law, one might thus expect the carrier to have an acceleration a, given by

$$a = \frac{F}{m} = \frac{qE}{m}$$

where m is the mass of the charge carrier.

For rather complicated reasons, however, which we shall not go into here, the mean acceleration for most materials is zero, and the numerical value v of the velocity of the charge carriers is (at constant temperature) proportional to the field strength E:

$$v = kE \tag{2.34}$$

The factor k is called the **mobility** of the charge carriers with the unit $\mathrm{m^2V^{-1}s^{-1}}$. In most materials only one type of charge carrier, with a given mobility k and concentration n, exists. An important exception to this rule is ionized air. We shall return to the special conditions relevant to this case in Section 17.

12. Conductivity and Resistivity

A transport of charges induced by an electric field is called an electric current. We define the **current density** j as the amount of charge passing through a unit area, perpendicular to the direction of flow, per unit time. j is a vector in the direction of flow of positive charges. If the concentration of mobile charge carriers is n, their charge q and their velocity is v, then the expression for j can be written

$$j = nqv \tag{2.35}$$

The current density refers to the conditions at a single point.

If we integrate j over the whole cross section S of the medium in which the charge flow takes place, we find the total current I. Mathematically, this may be expressed as

$$I = \int_S j \cdot dS \tag{2.36}$$

The unit for current is the ampere (A), which is a fundamental SI unit. Current density is thus expressed as $\mathrm{A \cdot m^{-2}}$.

According to (2.34), equation (2.35) may be written

$$j = nqkE \tag{2.37}$$

where q is the numerical value of the charge on the carriers. The quantity

$$\gamma = nqk \tag{2.38}$$

is called the (volume or bulk) **conductivity** of the material considered. Equation (2.37) may thus be formulated as

$$j = \gamma E \tag{2.39}$$

Equation (2.39) is often written

$$E = \rho j \tag{2.40}$$

The quantity $\rho = 1/\gamma$ is called the volume **resistivity** of the material. The mobility k and concentration n of the charge carriers are constant for most materials, so γ (and ρ) are also constant (for constant temperature) for a range of values of E. Equation (2.39) can thus be stated as: *The current density is proportional to the electrical field strength*. This relation is called **Ohm's law**.

The unit of conductivity is A/(Vm) or $\Omega^{-1}m^{-1}$. The unit of resistivity is Ωm, because V/A is called Ω (ohm). Table 2.2 shows the resistivity at room temperature of some commonly used materials.

13. Conductance and Resistance

The material properties, conductivity and resistivity, refer to the region around a single point in a material. They are thus differential quantities, and as such, they are normally not accessible to direct measurements but must be deduced from the determination of other quantities of integral nature. This is probably best explained by a simple example.

Table 2.2. Volume resistivity (at room temperature) of some commonly used materials

Material	Volume resistivity $\Omega \cdot m$
Silver	$1.6 \cdot 10^{-8}$
Copper	$1.7 \cdot 10^{-8}$
Aluminum	$2.9 \cdot 10^{-8}$
Iron	$1.0 \cdot 10^{-7}$
1 N HCl	$1.0 \cdot 10^{-2}$
Distilled water	10^4
Celluloid	$2 \cdot 10^8$
Dry wood	$3 \cdot 10^8$
Glass (dry)	$2 \cdot 10^{11}$
Plexiglass	$1 \cdot 10^{13}$
Rubber	$3 \cdot 10^{14}$
Quartz	$5 \cdot 10^{16}$
Polystyrene	$1 \cdot 10^{17}$

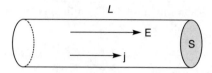

Figure 2.18 Current density and electric field

Let us (see Figure 2.18) consider a cylindrical conductor of cross section S, length L, and volume conductivity γ. If an electric field E is established in the material, an electric current I will flow in the direction of the field. The current I can be written

$$I = jS$$

where the current density j is given by

$$j = \gamma E$$

or

$$I = \gamma SE \qquad (2.41)$$

Equation (2.41) may now be written

$$I = \gamma \frac{S}{L} EL \qquad (2.42)$$

If the material is homogeneous the field strength is constant along the conductor and EL is, according to equation (2.13), equal to the potential difference V between the ends of the conductor, and equation (2.42) can be formulated as

$$I = GV \qquad (2.43)$$

The quantity

$$G = \gamma \frac{S}{L} \qquad (2.44)$$

is called the **conductance** of the conductor. According to (2.43), the unit of conductance is ampere/volt, or siemens (S), i.e.,

$$1\,S = 1\,A \cdot V^{-1}$$

Equation (2.44) can also be written

$$V = \frac{1}{G} I$$

or

$$V = RI \qquad (2.45)$$

where

$$R = \frac{1}{G}$$

or

$$R = \rho \frac{L}{S} \tag{2.46}$$

R is called the **resistance** of the conductor. The resistance is thus the reciprocal of the conductance. The unit of resistance is volt/ampere, which is called ohm (Ω), i.e.,

$$1\,\Omega = 1\,V \cdot A^{-1}$$

By measuring V and I, the resistance R, characteristic for the particular conductor, is determined from equation (2.45), and the resistivity ρ, characteristic for the material, from equation (2.46).

Although equation (2.45) is derived for a special, simple case, it expresses a general relation for all current paths, which can be stated as follows: *The ratio between the voltage difference between two points and the current flowing between the same two points is equal to a constant, the resistance, characteristic for the current path. The resistance can, for isotropic, homogenous media, be written as the product of the resistivity and a geometrical factor with the dimension of reciprocal length.* This is the integral (or household) version of **Ohm's law**.

EXAMPLE 2.8:

A conductor (see Figure 2.18) has a cross section $S = 1\text{ mm}^2 = 10^{-6}\text{ m}^2$ and a length $L = 10$ m. A voltage difference $V = 0.08$ V across the length of the conductor releases a current $I = 0.5$ A through the conductor. According to equation (2.45) the conductor has a resistance

$$R = \frac{V}{I} = \frac{0.08}{0.5} = 0.16\,\Omega$$

and a resistivity

$$\rho = R\frac{S}{L} = 0.16\,\frac{10^{-6}}{10} = 1.6 \cdot 10^{-8}\,\Omega \cdot m$$

(The conductor is probably silver.)

14. Surface Conductivity and Resistivity

In Section 13 the transport of charge through the bulk of a material was discussed. In the static electric context, however, charge transport often takes place along the surface or in a thin surface layer of a charged body, usually to a grounded electrode in contact with the surface. This process is normally described by introducing the **surface conductivity** γ_s (and corresponding **surface resistivity** ρ_s). If an electric field is applied with a component E_s along the surface, a current with the **linear current density** j_s will flow in the direction of E_s. The surface conductivity is then defined by

$$j_s = \gamma_s E_s \qquad (2.47)$$

and correspondingly, for the surface resistivity ρ_s,

$$E_s = \rho_s j_s \qquad (2.48)$$

because

$$\rho_s = \frac{1}{\gamma_s}$$

As j_s is a **linear** current density, the unit is ampere/meter, Am^{-1}, and not Am^{-2} as is the case for a conventional (area) current density. The unit for E_s is Vm^{-1}; consequently the unit for γ_s is $AV^{-1} = \Omega^{-1}$ and for ρ_s the unit is $VA^{-1} = \Omega$.

15. Surface Conductance and Surface Resistance

If a voltage difference V_s applied between two electrodes placed on the surface of a body releases a current I_s between the electrodes, a surface conductance G_s and a surface resistance R_s are defined respectively by

$$I_s = G_s V_s \qquad (2.49)$$

and

$$V_s = R_s I_s \qquad (2.50)$$

With suitable electrode geometry, equation (2.50) can be derived from equation (2.48); thus the differential material property ρ_s can be deduced from the measurable integral quantity R_s.

In Figure 2.19 are shown two electrodes of length a placed parallel to each other at a distance b on the surface of a material. A voltage source V_s makes a current I_s flow between the electrodes. The field E_s and the linear current density j_s between the electrodes are approximately given by

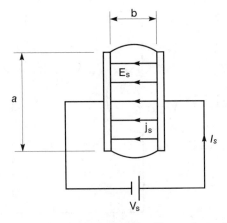

Figure 2.19 Surface resistivity, linear electrodes

$$E_s = \frac{V_s}{b} \quad \text{and} \quad j_s = \frac{I_s}{a}$$

Equation (2.48) may thus be written

$$\frac{V_s}{b} = \rho_s \frac{I_s}{a}$$

or according to equation (2.50)

$$\rho_s = \frac{V_s}{I_s}\frac{a}{b} = R_s \frac{a}{b} \tag{2.51}$$

Why Not Ohms per Square?

It appears from equation (2.51) that if the electrode spacing b is chosen equal to the electrode length a, i.e., if the electrodes are forming a square, the surface resistivity ρ_s will be equal to the surface resistance R_s. In certain parts of the world, this has given rise to the unfortunate, misleading and completely unnecessary interpretation that surface resistivity is measured in the mongrel mixture of units and geometrical concepts, *ohm(s) per square*. There is of course no system of units where a square is a unit, and as shown above a square does not appear naturally in the derivation of equation (2.51).

The misleading habit of expressing surface resistivity in ohm per square instead of the unit ohm, required by the definition in equation (2.48), is bypassed by using a different system of measuring conditions than the linear electrode system, shown in Figure 2.19.

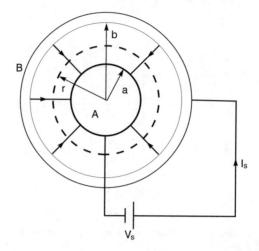

Figure 2.20 Surface resistivity, cylindrical electrodes

Let the cylindrical electrodes A and B be placed on a surface (see Figure 2.20). The radii of the inner and outer electrodes are a and b, respectively. If a voltage difference V_s is applied between the electrodes, the field strength E_s at a point at a distance r $(a < r < b)$ from the axis is given by

$$E_s = \frac{V_s}{r \ln \frac{b}{a}} \tag{2.52}$$

If the voltage difference V_s causes a current I_s to flow between the electrodes, the current density j_s at the distance r is

$$j_s = \frac{I}{2\pi r} \tag{2.53}$$

From equations (2.48), (2.50), (2.52), and (2.53) we thus find that

$$\rho_s = \frac{V_s}{I_s} \frac{2\pi}{\ln \frac{b}{a}} = R_s \frac{2\pi}{\ln \frac{b}{a}} \tag{2.54}$$

The advantage of using cylindrical electrodes is primarily that the field and current density between the electrodes are better defined than they are with linear electrodes. And of course equation (2.54) also shows, like the definition in equation (2.48), that surface resistivity is measured in Ω, *nothing more, nothing less*. The practical execution of surface resistivity measurements will be discussed in Chapter 6, Section 3.

16. Decay of Charge

Static electricity is often defined as the behavior of electric charges at rest on insulators or isolated conductors. Nevertheless, an important part of this science deals with the movement of charges under the action of their own fields, spreading or neutralizing the charges, and making the fields decay. In any kind of charge decay some sort of conducting path, containing mobile charge carriers, has to be established from the location of the charge to, normally, ground. Although the decay is always described by the same basic formulas, equations (2.39) and (2.40), it is convenient to distinguish three different types of decay schemes:

(1) Charge decay of a capacitive system, i.e., an isolated conductor characterized by its capacitance C and resistance R with respect to ground.

(2) Charge decay of a nonconducting system, where the charge is located on a semi-insulative material with a given resistivity ρ and permittivity ε, and where the charge transport takes place exclusively through the material itself.

(3) Charge decay through the air.

These are discussed in the following sections.

Charge Decay of Capacitive System

An isolated conductor may be characterized electrically by its capacitance C and leakage resistance R, both with respect to ground. Such an arrangement is called a capacitive system. The resistance R may, primarily, be a well-defined resistance of a resistor or the odd and normally rather uncertain (insulation) resistance of the supports for the conductor. It is a special characteristic for the decay of charge on a conducting system that the contact between the conductor and the resistive path only needs to be established at a single point. If the only resistive way from the conductor to ground is through the surrounding air, special conditions may prevail, as explained below.

The capacitance C is an integral measure of the distribution of the electric field, or rather the electrical flux, from a given charge on the conductor between the conductor and ground. The capacitance will thus depend upon the location of the conductor and may change somewhat if the conductor itself or other neighboring conductors are moved. Both the resistance and capacitance, however, are accessible for direct measurements.

Let the conductor, A (see Figure 2.21), with capacitance C and resistance to ground R, be charged initially with the charge q_0, giving rise to an initial voltage $V_0 = q_0/C$. The conductor will be surrounded by an electric field E, which at any time is proportional to the charge q and the voltage V. A current $I = V/R$ will flow to ground, making the charge decrease at the rate $-dq/dt = I$. Consequently, the charge will change with time as

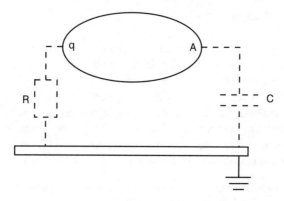

Figure 2.21 Charge decay of capacitive system

$$q = q_0 \exp\left(-\frac{t}{\tau}\right) \tag{2.55}$$

where the **time constant** $\tau = RC$. As the voltage V and the field strength E around the conductor are proportional to the charge q, these quantities will decrease, or decay, at the same rate.

EXAMPLE 2.9:

A conductor is insulated by a material giving it a resistance to ground of $R = 10^{11}$ Ω. The capacitance of the conductor is 200 pF. A charge $q_0 = 10^{-6}$ C is placed on the conductor. The initial voltage of the conductor is

$$V_0 = \frac{10^{-6}}{200 \cdot 10^{-12}} = 5000 \text{ V}$$

and the initial leakage or decay current is

$$I_0 = \frac{V_0}{R} = \frac{5000}{10^{11}} = 5 \cdot 10^{-8} \text{ A}$$

The field strength around the conductor will be proportional to the voltage, but the exact value at a given point cannot be calculated unless the total geometry and dielectric conditions are known.

If the distance from the conductor to ground is $d = 1$ m along some arbitrarily chosen path, the initial mean field strength along this path is

$$E_{m0} = \frac{V_0}{d} = \frac{5000}{1} = 5000 \text{ V} \cdot \text{m}^{-1}$$

The time constant for the system is

$$\tau = RC = 10^{11} \cdot 200 \cdot 10^{-12} = 20 \text{ s}$$

and thus the voltage, the current, and the field strength at any point around the conductor will have decayed to $1/e = 37\%$ of the initial values in 20 s.

Incidental Decay of Capacitive System

If a charged capacitive system is suddenly connected to ground through a low resistance the charge will decay as a fast current pulse, which may be destructive, if it happens to pass through a sensitive semiconductor component. The characteristics and the effect of the pulse depend upon the capacitive and resistive properties of the charged system. The problem of dealing with various discharge situations, like *the charged device model (CDM)* and *the human body model (HBM),* will be discussed in Chapter 4, Static Electric Effects.

17. Charge Decay of Nonconductors

As we have suggested for charged (isolated) conductors, it is possible to directly measure the parameters resistance and capacitance, determining the rate of decay of the charge and voltage of and consequently the field around the conductor.

In many situations, however, we have to deal with charged insulators or semi-insulators for which the charge decay may depend in a rather complex, and in practice unmeasurable, way on the geometrical and dielectric and resistive conditions of the environment.

In Figure 2.22a is shown a sample of a material with resistivity ρ and permittivity ε resting on a grounded plane. A charge q_0 is distributed uniformly over the area A giving a surface charge density of

$$\sigma_0 = \frac{q_0}{A}$$

If we assume the distance to other conductors in the surroundings to be much larger than the thickness d of the sample, the field from the charge will be directed toward the grounded plane and will have the value

$$E_0 = \frac{\sigma_0}{\varepsilon}$$

neglecting the stray field at the edge of the charge distribution. The field E will cause a decay current to flow with a density j given by

$$E = \rho j$$

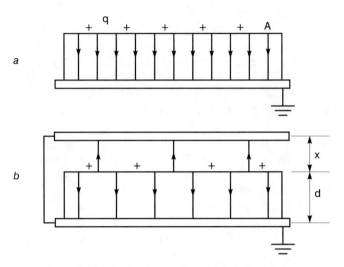

Figure 2.22 Charge decay of semi-insulating system

but because

$$j = -\frac{d\sigma}{dt}$$

equation (2.40) may be written

$$E = \rho \bar{\jmath}$$

$$\frac{\sigma}{\varepsilon} = -\rho\frac{d\sigma}{dt} \tag{2.56}$$

with the solution

$$\sigma = \sigma_0\exp\left(-\frac{t}{\tau_0}\right) \tag{2.57}$$

and the time constant

$$\tau_0 = \rho\varepsilon \tag{2.58}$$

This result is generally valid for all situations where the field from the charge extends only through one medium with the parameters ρ and ε.

In Figure 2.22b a grounded plate is placed parallel with the charged semi-insulator, at a distance x in a vacuum (or air). Part of the flux from the charge now extends through the vacuum <u>where no decay current will flow</u>, so the decay <u>process will be slower.</u> By expressing that the integral of the field strength from a point on the charged surface to ground is the same through the medium with permittivity ε and through the vacuum with permittivity ε_0 (this integral is equal to

ρ: volume resistivity
ε: permittivity

the potential of the point considered), it can be shown that the decay is still exponential, but now with a time constant of

$$\tau = \rho\varepsilon + \rho\varepsilon_0 \frac{d}{x} = \tau_0\left(1 + \frac{d}{\varepsilon_r x}\right) \tag{2.59}$$

where ε_r is the relative permittivity of the charged material.

Equation (2.59) states, for a special case, that the decay of charge on a semi-insulative material is not only determined by the material parameters but also by the geometry and the dielectric and resistive properties of the surroundings, and is only determined in a predictable way in special cases like the one described here. This is essentially also the case when we consider the decay of charge on a capacitive system, as described under (a), but in this case the quantities R and C determining the rate of decay, although they may vary, can at least in principle be measured.

EXAMPLE 2.10:

A sample of plexiglass with a thickness $d = 0.01$ m is resting on a grounded plane (see Figure 2.22a). The distance to other conductors is much larger than the thickness of the sample. A positive charge is distributed uniformly over the surface of the sample with a surface density $\sigma = 10^{-7}$ C $\cdot$ m^{-2}. From Tables 2.1 and 2.2, we have $\varepsilon_r = 3.4$ (i.e., $\varepsilon = \varepsilon_0\varepsilon_r = 3 \cdot 10^{-11}$ C^{2}N^{-1}m^{-2}). The initial field strength in the sample is

[margin annotation: Volume resistivity $1 \times 10^{13}\,\Omega\cdot m$; relative permittivity $\varepsilon_r = 3.4$]

$$E_0 = \frac{\sigma_0}{\varepsilon} = \frac{10^{-7}}{3 \cdot 10^{-11}} = 3.3 \cdot 10^3 \text{ V} \cdot \text{m}^{-1}$$

The initial surface potential of the sample is

$$V_{0s} = E_0 d = 3.3 \cdot 10^3 \cdot 0.01 = 33 \text{ V}$$

The initial current density is

$$j_0 = \frac{E_0}{\rho} = \frac{3.3 \cdot 10^3}{10^{13}} = 3.3 \cdot 10^{-10} \text{ A} \cdot \text{m}^{-2}$$

The time constant τ_0 for the system is

$$\tau_0 = \varepsilon\rho = 3 \cdot 10^{-11} \cdot 10^{13} = 300 \text{ s}$$

If a grounded plate is placed above the plexiglass sample (see Figure 2.22b) at a distance $x = 0.003$ m, the time constant is now

$$\tau = \tau_0\left(1 + \frac{d}{\varepsilon_r x}\right) = 300 \cdot \left(1 + \frac{0.01}{3.4 \cdot 0.003}\right) = 594 \text{ s}$$

It thus takes about twice as long for the charge to decay in this situation, because the field strength and consequently the decay current (density) are only about half their values from the situation in Figure 2.22a.

Charge Decay Through the Air, I

If a charge is located on an insulator there is in principle no way by which the charge may ever be removed. If, however, the charged insulator is completely surrounded by a conducting fluid in contact with all points of the surface, the charge or the field from the charge may be neutralized by oppositely charged ions being attracted to the insulator. Although this scenario in principle could be established by using a conducting liquid, the only practical solution is to surround the charged body with (ionized) air. In order to be able to describe such a situation, it is necessary to give an overview of the electrical characteristics of ionized air.

Electrical properties of ionized air

In any solid or liquid material, the charge, mobility, and concentration of possible charge carriers are constant (at constant temperature), as long as electrical breakdown does not take place. In a metallic conductor, the charge carriers are (valence) electrons with a concentration characteristic for the metal in question; in a semiconductor the carriers may be (positive) holes. But the carriers are always there to yield a current, when a field is applied. They do not have to be produced somewhere else and brought to the site where they are needed, and their characteristics, like mobility and concentration, do not change during the process. As a consequence, the conductivity

$$\gamma = nqk$$

can be ascribed a constant value during the decay.

But the situation is not this simple when a gas is the current-carrying medium. Gases inherently contain no or very few nonpaired charges that can be moved independently by an electric field to cause a net current. Gases in general and, more specifically in the present context, atmospheric air can be ionized, i.e., made to contain mobile charge carriers (see Section 9 p. 24).

Atmospheric ions, however, differ from the charge carriers in other media in several ways. Although the naturally occurring air ions are produced almost homogeneously throughout the air volume by radioactive radiation, for technical use, where much larger concentrations than the natural ones are needed, the ions are produced locally by some ionization device, electrical or radioactive, and have to be transported to the site where they are needed for neutralization.

The concentration of air ions will change with time and location because of processes like recombination with other, oppositely charged, ions, combination with particles, and plateout on surfaces, or simply because the actual field-induced neutralization process may deplete the air of ions faster than they are resupplied by the ionizing device.

The mobility of the air ions may change because the same combination processes can create large or heavy ions with lower mobilities; thus, the ions may not have discrete mobilities but be distributed over a large range of mobilities. And as the neutralizing effect depends upon the air containing ions of opposite polarity of the charge to be neutralized, it is necessary to introduce polar conductivities, i.e., conductivities caused by positive and negative ions, respectively.

We define a function of distribution $f(k)$ so that the concentration of ions dn with mobilities between k and $k + dk$ is given by

$$dn = f(k)dk \qquad (2.60)$$

If the common (numerical) charge of the ions is q, the conductivity γ of the air is

$$\gamma = q \int_0^\infty kf(k)dk \qquad (2.61)$$

For practical purposes, atmospheric ions may be divided into two groups, small ions with mobility k_s and large ions with mobility k_l. If the corresponding concentrations are n_s and n_l, respectively, the conductivity may be written

$$\gamma = q(k_s n_s + k_l n_l) \qquad (2.62)$$

Because the mobilities of large ions are maybe 1000 times smaller than those of small ions, and because the charge on a small ion is the electronic charge e, equation (2.62) may with good approximation be written

$$\gamma \approx ek_s n_s \qquad (2.63)$$

As will be discussed in the next section, only one polarity of ions participates in the neutralization of a given charge. We therefore introduce the positive and negative polar conductivities

$$\gamma^+ = ek_s^+ n_s^+ \qquad (2.64)$$

and

$$\gamma^- = ek_s^- n_s^- \qquad (2.65)$$

where k_s^+ ($\approx 1.4 \cdot 10^{-4}\,\text{m}^2 \cdot \text{V}^{-1}\text{s}^{-1}$) and n_s^+ are the mobility and concentration of small positive ions, and k_s^- ($\approx 1.9 \cdot 10^{-4}\,\text{m}^2 \cdot \text{V}^{-1}\text{s}^{-1}$) and n the corresponding quantities for small negative ions.

It may be somewhat misleading to talk about a negative conductivity, because γ^- also is a positive quantity producing a current in the direction of the field, as does γ^+, although the charge carriers move in the opposite direction. Corresponding to the polar conductivities we define the polar resistivities

$$\rho^+ = \frac{1}{\gamma^+} \tag{2.66}$$

and

$$\rho^- = \frac{1}{\gamma^-} \tag{2.67}$$

Charge Decay Through the Air, II

In Figure 2.23 is shown a positively charged conductor S, surrounded by ionized air with the polar resistivities ρ^+ and ρ^-. At a site of the surface where the charge density is σ^+ the field strength in front of S is

$$E = \frac{\sigma}{\varepsilon_0}$$

The field will cause a current of positive ions with density

$$j^+ = \frac{E}{\rho^+} \tag{2.68}$$

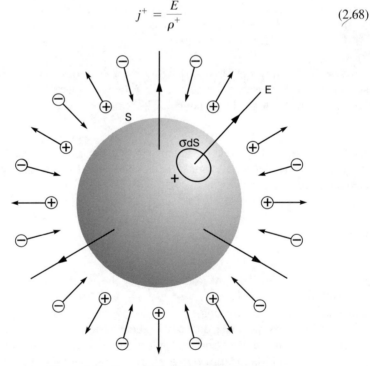

Figure 2.23 Charged body in conducting air

to flow away from S and a current of negative ions with density

$$j^- = \frac{E}{\rho^-} \tag{2.69}$$

to flow towards S.

The current of positive ions, given by (2.68), will not affect the charge on S. The current of negative ions, on the other hand, will cause σ^+ to decrease with the rate given by (2.69), i.e.,

$$j^- = \frac{E}{\rho^-} = \frac{\sigma^+}{\varepsilon_0 \rho^-} = -\frac{d\sigma^+}{dt} \tag{2.70}$$

This is the same as equation (2.56), and if ρ^- can be considered to be constant, the solution is

$$\sigma^+ = \sigma_0^+ \exp\left(-\frac{t}{\tau^+}\right) \tag{2.71}$$

where σ_0^+ is the initial value of the positive surface charge density, and the time constant τ^+ is given by

$$\tau^+ = \varepsilon_0 \rho^- \tag{2.72}$$

Correspondingly, the charge on a negatively charged conductor will decay with a time constant τ^- given by

$$\tau^- = \varepsilon_0 \rho^+ \tag{2.73}$$

Equations (2.72) and (2.73) express the obvious fact that positive charges are neutralized by negative charges and vice versa, or that the rate of decay of positive charges is determined by the "negative" resistivity.

The preceding formulas are derived under the assumption that the charge in question is located on a conductor. Only in this case can we be sure that the field in front of a given charge density is given by equation (2.10). Experience, however, shows that for the same geometry with respect to grounded surroundings and for the same ionization conditions, charges decay essentially with the same rate, whether they are located on conductors or on insulators. It should, on the other hand, also be pointed out that the time constants calculated by (2.72) and (2.73) are normally much shorter than what is found experimentally. This may be caused by the fact that the neutralizing currents, given by equations (2.69) and (2.70), deplete the air for ions, i.e., make both resistivities increase, and thereby reduce the rate of decay of the charge. This effect is best understood in the case where the charged body is placed close to grounded surroundings. A major part of the flux of the charge will then be located in the region between the body and ground, and if the ions in this region are not supplied sufficiently fast, the field from the charge will cause the depletion of ions in the air and consequently a slowing down of the neutralization.

Removal of Ions from the Air

An air ion is, in contrast to most other charge carriers, a unstable structure and consequently has a limited lifetime. It may, as we have explained, be moved to some surface (oppositely charged or grounded) where it may be neutralized. It may combine with oppositely charged ions or particles and hence cease to exist as an ion. Or a small ion (with high mobility) may combine with aerosol particles and then either be neutralized or become a large ion (with low mobility); in both cases it again no longer exists as a small ion. The rate of combination is proportional to the concentration of the species involved. (See Figure 2.24.)

Let us as an example consider a room with a small ion concentration of, say 1000 cm^{-3}, and a low aerosol concentration of similar magnitude.

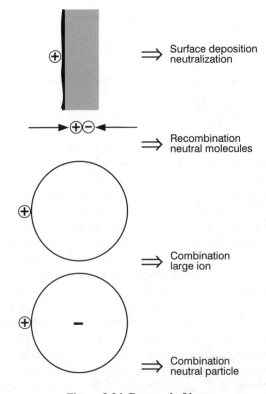

Figure 2.24 Removal of ions

If now a candle or a cigarette is lit in the room, the aerosol concentration may almost instantaneously rise to maybe 100,000 cm^{-3}, and the small ion concentration may decrease to maybe 50–100 cm^{-3}, because most of the small ions have combined with the aerosol particles produced by the combustion processes. Although the total (small plus large) ion concentration has hardly changed, it appears from equations (2.62) and (2.63) that the conductivity has been reduced by a factor of 10–20. This inverse relation between conductivity and particle concentration can be used as an indicator of the particle level in the air.

Chapter 3

Static Electrification

As explained in Chapter 2, two bodies interacting with electrical forces are said to be electrically charged, or to have an electric charge. The main scope of this chapter is to explain how a body or material obtains such a charge.

First of all, charges are never generated. They exist all the time as positive charges of the protons in the nuclei of atoms and as negative charges of the electrons around the nuclei. But only when the electrons are removed from some of the atoms in one material and transferred to the atoms in another, or maybe even in the same, material do we see an electrical effect, most conveniently described by the electric field. And again we see this effect only if the electron-exchanging materials are separated from each other in such a way that the charges do not reunite during the separation process.

The transfer of electrons between atoms or molecules may occur when two solid materials, identical or different, contact and possibly rub against each other, with electrons crossing the interface in a preferential direction, giving one material a positive and the other a negative excess charge. The exchange of electrons may also occur when an insulating liquid is flowing through a tube, or when a liquid of almost any type is breaking up into droplets of nonuniform magnitude or falling through an inhomogenous electric field, as in a thundercloud.

1. Charging of Solids

Triboelectrification

The most important type of charge separation involves the contact and friction between solid materials, known as **triboelectrification**.

Metals

If two metallic surfaces are brought into contact with each other, a voltage difference is established across the interface. This is called the **contact potential difference**, and for most metals it has a value ranging from a couple of tenths of a volt to a few volts. The contact potential difference is established because electrons in the contacting metals are in different states of energy; i.e., the work required to remove a (loosely bound) electron (the **work function**) is different for the two metals. As a result, electrons will flow to the metal with the highest work function where the electron energy is lowest. The transport of electrons stops when the energy levels (Fermi levels) have the same height in the two metals. The voltage difference between the metals is then equal to the difference in work functions divided by the electronic charge.

This process may take place when the distance between the two metal surfaces is sufficiently small, i.e., less than about 2–3 nm, even at just a single point. It should be mentioned here that charge separation caused by contact between metals only may produce normal static electric effects, when the separation of the metals involved is very fast, for instance if metal dust is blown against an isolated metal surface.

Insulators

It is likely that processes similar to the ones described above for metals take place during contact between materials of which one or both are insulators. It is, however, difficult to completely characterize an insulating surface. In many materials, and especially in noncrystalline materials, the energy levels are badly defined, and the contact processes are therefore not known in detail.

It is conceivable that only electrons located close to the surface can participate in the charging of highly insulating materials. For some of these materials it is possible, similar to metals, to measure the work function for loosely bound electrons. The practical implication of this, however, is not great, mostly because the measured values only hold for materials with well-defined surface states. As soon as a surface that may have been prepared in vacuum is exposed to "ordinary" air, its state, including the energy levels of "surface electrons," may change considerably. Consequently, charging experiments involving insulators can only be expected to yield quantitatively predictable results if the surfaces are carefully prepared and the experiments performed in vacuum. Such experiments may disclose very little about what one can expect to find under more practical conditions.

Contact Electrification

One of the material parameters influencing the course of a charging process taking place between two solid materials is the permittivity. The permittivity of a material is defined as the ratio between corresponding values of dielectric displacement and electric field strength. However, in the present context it is of more importance that the permittivity is also a measure of the ability of the material to become polarized in an electric field.

An ion or other charged small atomic or molecular cluster landing on an insulating surface will be bound to the surface by polarization forces; the stronger the forces, the higher the permittivity of the insulator. This is the background for **Coehn's law**, which states that when two materials are in contact with each other, the one with the highest permittivity will become positive. This law, which also seems to imply that the charged particles exchanged are positive, was originally based on a comparison of known values of permittivities and published **triboelectric series**, i.e., lists of materials arranged in such an order that any material will become positively charged when rubbed against another material that is nearer the negative end of the series. There is no doubt that such a correlation exists, but with quite a few exceptions, and certain groups of materials may even be arranged in a closed series.

Table 3.1 shows an example of a triboelectric series. Such series should be used with some caution, as the order of the materials may differ from one series to the next. It is possible, from the relative positions in a triboelectric series, to predict the sharing of **polarity**, but the **magnitude** of the charges separated by contact and friction between two given materials can only be predicted with a high degree of uncertainty. However, the magnitude of the charges increases with the degree of friction between the materials. The reason for this could be that the rubbing will tend to increase the area of contact between the surfaces, and that the charging process itself is governed only by the energy state of the surfaces, and charged particles will cross the interface at points of sufficient proximity. This, however, is hardly a satisfactory interpretation, because then it would not be possible to explain the fact that two identical surfaces may get charged by being rubbed against each other, although it could be argued that no two surfaces are ever identical and that incidental and uncontrollable differences might cause a different affinity to the charged particles.

Asymmetric Friction

As mentioned above, the degree of friction during contact between two materials will influence the contact area and thus the exchange of charges. But the process of friction may have a specific influence of its own. It can be demonstrated that if two, macroscopically speaking, identical surfaces are rubbed against each other in

Table 3.1. Triboelectric series

Positive end
Plexiglass
Bakelite
Cellulose acetate
Glass
Quartz
Nylon
Wool
Silk
Cotton
Paper
Amber
Resins (natural and manmade)
Metals
Rubber
Acetate rayon
Dacron
Orlon
Polystyrene
Teflon
Cellulose nitrate
Polyvinyl chloride
Negative end

higher permittivity
" (dielectric constant)

such a way that the contact takes place between a small area of one surface and a larger area of the other, the polarities of the surfaces are likely to change, if the roles of the surfaces are interchanged. This is called **asymmetric friction**, and it seems to indicate that the friction itself may be vital for the charge exchange.

A possible explanation is that the asymmetry may cause a thermal gradient to develop between the surfaces and thus induce already existing charge carriers to move in a certain direction, or the charge carriers may even be produced by a thermal dissociation of the material into charged components. Other conditions than those mentioned above may also play a role in the charge exchange between contacting solid materials, such as the existence of (external) electric fields across interfaces. This effect may be utilized in electrostatic separation.

Postcontact Processes

Although contact between metals may produce a charge transfer, no net charge will remain on the metals after separation, unless at least one of the metals is insulated, and the separation happens very quickly. If, on the other hand, at least one of the materials is an insulator, both surfaces will be charged immediately after the separation, and if they are both insulating, or one of them is an isolated conductor, the charges may remain on the materials, even when they are far removed from each other.

During the initial part of the separation of the surfaces, the field strength between the positive and negative charges may exceed the breakdown field strength. A discharge (spark or other type) may then take place and reunite part of the separated charges, thus reducing the magnitude of the charges remaining on the surfaces. If one of the materials is a grounded conductor, the charge left there after the separation will distribute itself to ground, when the distance to the opposite charge is so large that the attraction between the charges separated is negligible.

2. Charging of Liquids

The charging of solid materials by contact and friction, as described in Section 1, is the best-known type of static electrification, but it is not the only one. Liquids may also become charged, for instance by flowing through pipes or by spraying, and if the liquids give off vapors to form explosive mixtures with atmospheric air or oxygen, explosions or ignition often result.

As early as 1870 it was shown by Helmholtz that phenomena like **electrophoresis** and **capillary electricity** in aqueous solutions can be explained, if it is assumed that on the interface between a liquid and a solid or between a liquid and a gas an electric double layer exists in the liquid, with a layer of charge close to the surface and an opposite charge at a short distance deeper inside the liquid.

This double layer is assumed to be formed in the following way: at the surface of the water some of the molecules, about 1 out of every 25, are arranged with the double-charged oxygen ions (O^{2-}) towards the surface and the single-charged hydrogen ions (H^+) inwards. This arrangement of molecular dipoles in itself forms an electrical double layer, but the charges cannot be separated by mechanical means, and the layer will not play any primary role in the generation of static electricity.

The positive (hydrogen) end, however, of the water dipoles will bind incidental free negative ions (anions) in the liquid, originating from dissociation of the liquid itself or from electrolytical impurities. These anions remain close to the surface because of their attraction to the water dipoles. The corresponding positive ions (cations) are loosely bound (to the anions) and are located deeper inside the liquid. It is this system of separable charges that constitutes the electrical double layer responsible for the static charging of liquids.

electric double layer ↙

Flow and Spraying

If the surface of a liquid (or the interface to a solid) is changed, the electric double layer has to be formed or destroyed. These processes are supposed to have a certain inertia, which implies that it is possible to separate the charges of the double layer by mechanical action on the liquid.

If a liquid is flowing through a tube, there is a certain tendency for the outer charge of the double layer to be given off to the tube and the inner charge to be brought along with the flow. The effect of the charging increases with the resistivity of the liquid (and depends on several other parameters, as we shall discuss later), and as a consequence only highly insulating liquids (for example, not water) will show charging by flowing.

It is an old experience that the breaking up of a liquid into droplets may produce charge separation. This is what happens with "waterfall" electricity, where the fine mist consisting primarily of very small droplets is predominantly negatively charged, and the larger water drops, precipitating more easily, are positive.

Charging of liquids by flow can only occur with highly insulating liquids, but charging by spraying can and normally will occur with almost any kind of liquids.

Charging of Liquids by Induction

When a liquid is exposed to an electric field, a net charge is induced on its surface, unless the resistivity of the liquid is very high, in which case polarization is the predominant process.

In the case shown in Figure 3.1, the charge bound by the field is negative. If a droplet of radius r is formed and removed from the surface, the droplet will carry with it a (negative) charge q approximately given by

$$q = \pi r^2 \, \varepsilon E \qquad (3.1)$$

where E is the strength of the applied field and ε is the permittivity of the gas above the liquid (normally equal to ε_0).

With this method it is possible to give droplets of almost any liquid positive as well as negative charges, and much larger charges than would be the case if the droplets were formed by mechanical methods in the absence of electric fields.

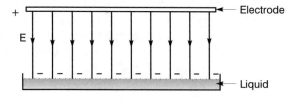

Figure 3.1 Charging by induction

Other Charging Processes

As long as we consider only incidental and unplanned charging, the processes we have described are the ones most commonly responsible for the charging. For scientific experiments or practical applications of static electricity, a series of more special charging processes may be applied. Among these are are charging by freezing, ion and electron bombardment, thermal electron emission, photoelectric effects, radioactive decay, and field emission.

3. Gases Never Charge!

It is not uncommon to find large static electric charges where gases are used in connection with transport of liquids and solids such as powders. This phenomenon is often misinterpreted as charging of the gas itself. But this is not the case.

Admittedly, an air molecule could be imagined to lose or gain an electron, i.e., become ionized by collision with other air molecules, with airborne particles, or with container walls. But for such an electron exchange to take place by collision, the molecule should have a kinetic energy far exceeding that corresponding to practical flow velocities or commonly encountered temperatures.

If, on the other hand, a gas contains liquid or solid particles, e.g., dust, such particles may become charged by mutual contact and friction, or more likely through friction with tube or container walls. But a particulate- and droplet-free gas cannot become charged by its own motion.

4. More About Charging Conditions

Although the course of a charging process, as already mentioned, is difficult, if at all possible, to predict from the knowledge of characteristic parameters of the materials involved, certain simple rules may be formulated concerning the likelihood of encountering major charge separations under given circumstances.

Solids

The level of a static charging is governed by two competing processes: the rate of charge separation and the rate of charge neutralization or decay. We can give general rules for the rate of charge separation only to a very limited degree. It is normally accepted that the rate of decay increases with decreasing resistivities of the materials involved. Except in cases where the transport of charges during the decay is limited to a surface layer, it is conceivable that the rate of decay is governed by the bulk resistivity and the permittivity of the material. As explained in Chapter 2, Section 17, a charge on a piece of material, in contact with grounded surroundings, with resistivity ρ and permittivity ε will normally decay with a time constant τ given by

$$\tau = \rho\varepsilon$$

EXAMPLE 3.1:

Let us consider a sample of a material resting on and in good contact with a grounded surface. The permittivity of the material is $\varepsilon = 3 \cdot 10^{-11}$ F $\cdot$ m^{-1} (i.e., $\varepsilon_r \approx 4$). If it is required that a charge on the material decays with a time constant $\tau = 0.01$ s (99% of the charge will have decayed in about 0.05 s), then, according to equation (2.58), the resistivity ρ of the material must fulfill the condition

$$\rho < \frac{\tau}{\varepsilon} = \frac{10^{-2}}{3 \cdot 10^{-11}} \approx 3 \cdot 10^8 \Omega \cdot m$$

The relative permittivities of many common materials fall within a rather narrow range (see Table 2.1), thus in principle it is easy to predict the (bulk) decay behavior of a given material if the bulk resistivity is known or measured. In practice, however, determination of bulk resistivity is often rather difficult when dealing with manufactured items like carrier trays, etc.

On the other hand, it is often possible and sometimes easy to determine the surface resistivity of materials, samples, and manufactured items. But it should be stressed that the relation in equation 2.58 has been developed for bulk properties (resistivity and permittivity), and that there is no theoretical basis for assuming a corresponding relationship between surface resistivity and surface decay time. Mathematically, this is due to the fact that Gauss' law (equation 2.4) cannot be derived for the two-dimensional case. An attempt to handle this problem would involve the introduction of a "surface permittivity," ε_s, with the dimension capacitance (unit F) in contrast to the normal dimension of ε, capacitance/unit length (unit F $\cdot$ m^{-1}), and such a quantity is hard to interpret physically.

Experimental determinations of corresponding values of surface resistivity and charge decay times do not normally suggest a strong relationship between the two quantities. This is probably at least partly due to the fact that a given charge surface density may lead to widely varying decay-causing fields, depending on the thickness of the charged sample, nearness of conducting items, etc. Nevertheless, the chargeability and static properties of solid materials are traditionally characterized by the surface resistivity, for whatever it is worth. The old (European) classification might look like the one presented in Table 3.2.

The names of the three groups may differ from one presentation to another, and the use of the old designation *astatic* is *almost* as archaic as the American (EPA) insistence in radiological contexts on using the outdated unit *curie* instead of the worldwide-accepted unit *becquerel*. A more modern grouping of materials is given in Table 3.3.

Table 3.2. Old surface resistivity classification

Material type	Surface resistivity
Static materials	$> 10^{14} \, \Omega$
Astatic materials	10^{14}–$10^{10} \, \Omega$
Antistatic materials	$< 10^{10} \, \Omega$

Table 3.3. Modern surface resistivity classification

Material type	Surface resistivity
Insulative materials	$> 10^{12} \, \Omega$
Static dissipative materials	10^{12}–$10^{5} \, \Omega$
Conductive materials	$< 10^{5} \, \Omega$

The division of materials into these groups should be taken only as a rule of thumb. It is true that most measurements of chargings of solid materials show that the level of charges separated do increase with the resistivity, but definitely not in an unambiguous way.

Although materials of low resistivity never charge unless the materials are separated extremely fast, there are many examples of highly resistive materials being brought into contact without showing any significant charges after separation. Undoubtedly the nature of the contact plays a role in the charging process. Normally the charges separated will be greater the more intimate the contact and friction is, and therefore smooth surfaces will often charge more then rough ones. When it is stated that materials of low resistivity do not charge, this is generally true only when both materials have low resistivity. If, for instance, an insulating sheet of plastic (Figure 3.2) is guided by a metal roller, the sheet as well as the roller may be charged, and if the roller is not grounded, both polarities of charge may be retained after separation.

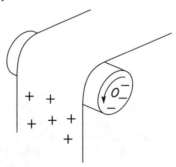

Figure 3.2 Charging between conductor and nonconductor

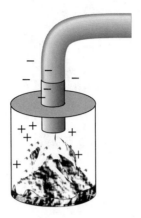

Figure 3.3 Charging of a powder

Dust, Powders

Dust and powders may be charged by contact and friction between the particles, especially if the individual particles have different properties, for instance, regarding size and/or material. A charging of this type may result in the particles sticking together. More common, however, are the processes where a powder is being transported through a system of tubes (see Figure 3.3), and the powder as a whole is being charged by friction with the walls of the tube system. This kind of charging may take place if either the powder or the tube or both are insulating.

The flow of charged powder can be considered as a current, and it has been demonstrated that for many types of powders the current increases with the square of the linear velocity or is even stronger, and may have values of several μA for a velocity of a few meter per second.

If the powder is collected in a isolated metal container, the current will charge the container to a voltage where the unavoidable decay current is equal to the charging current. We shall treat this problem in Chapter 5, Section 7.

Liquids

As mentioned earlier, the electrical double layer on the surface of many liquids can be partly separated by flow and spraying. If the liquid is flowing through a tube, the separated charges constitute a current to the container in which the liquid is being collected (see Figure 3.4).

Because the specific charge (charge per unit volume) of the liquid often depends very little on the velocity, the charging current is more or less proportional to the flow rate of the liquid. The specific charge generally increases with decreasing tube diameter, and flow through a filter, which can be considered as a

Figure 3.4 Charging of a liquid by flow

large number of (parallel) narrow tubes, will consequently often cause chargings. The specific charge also depends strongly on the resistivity of the liquid. As a rule of thumb, only liquids with resistivities above $10^7 \, \Omega \cdot$ m will produce essential static chargings because of flow.

But small amounts of additives may change the specific charge rather drastically. As an example, adding water to, for instance, toluene to form a disperse mixture makes the specific charge increase considerably although the resistivity is nearly constant. As examples of specific charges, diesel oil may have a value of 10^{-6}–$10^{-5} \, C \cdot m^{-3}$ and aviation gasoline about $10^{-4} \, C \cdot m^{-3}$.

Although only liquids of high resistivity charge by flowing, almost any liquid can produce charge separation by spraying, and the spray can charge any isolated conducting system it hits or can form space charges with fields, which under special circumstances can produce dangerous discharges. This is believed to have been the case with explosions in oil tankers during tank washing.

Chapter 4

Static Electric Effects

In Chapter 3 we have discussed the principal ways in which electrical charges can be separated. After separation, the charges may be located on insulators or isolated conductors. All effects of such static charge distributions are caused by the forces upon and between themselves or induced charges on grounded or ungrounded conductors, or by the forces from the charge distributions on airborne charge carriers, i.e., ions and electrons. Although all static electric effects are thus related to the forces between charges, it is practical to divide the description of the effects into the following two groups:

- *Mechanical effects.* Involving situations where bodies or particles, charged or polarized, are exposed to electrical forces comparable to or greater than their own weight.
- *Electrical effects.* Involving the field-induced intermedium motion of already existing charge carriers, either producing ionization and discharge phenomena or just causing noncarrier-producing currents.

1. Mechanical Effects

Mechanical effects appear mainly where light materials are being used. Some examples of such effects are:

- *Repulsion between like charges.* If fibers or threads in a bundle or plastic or paper sheets in a stack are being charged with the same polarity, they will repel each other and can be extremely difficult to handle.
- *Attraction between opposite charges.* When a charged length of paper, plastic, cloth, etc., is passing by a conductor, an opposite charge will be induced on the conductor, and the charged material may be pulled from its normal position and cling to the conductor. Other examples are charged clothing clinging to the body or powder sticking to transport tubes or containers.
- *Attraction of airborne particles to charged materials.* Airborne particles like dust may, either because they are charged or because they become polarized by nearby charged materials, be attracted to these materials and stick to the charged surfaces.

59

An example of this effect is the attraction of dust to wafers during production, where even the extremely low particle concentration in a clean room may be harmful if no precautions to neutralize the wafer charges are taken. It is also this effect that causes the plateout of dust on TV screens and monitors and also on the faces of operators sitting close to the screen. This phenomenon will be discussed in Chapter 7, Section 2.

2. Electrical Effects

For many years static electricity was considered to have only one detrimental effect of any importance: It produced sparks that could give unpleasant shocks or even cause explosions. This is a typical example of an ionization process in which charge carriers, electrons, in an electric field are accelerated to such velocities that they "reproduce" and may dissipate considerable amounts of energy, sometimes causing destruction of the material through which the carriers move, or initiating chemical processes like combustion. If the field strength is low enough, no extra charge carriers, or ions, are produced, and the static electric processes, i.e., the separation and eventual recombination of charges, will only result in relatively weak transient currents in the materials surrounding the location of the charges.

Actually, well into the electronic age these weak signals were considered to be without any kind of harmful effects. But with the development of more and more sensitive semiconductor devices, it was gradually realized that, at least in the world of electronic components and devices, the upper limits for acceptable static electric field strengths, voltages, and signal current peaks had to be lowered considerably. These limits are still being lowered. Therefore, making a careful evaluation of the static environment and, maybe even more, a basic understanding of the fundamental concepts of this environment necessary for a successful handling of present and future electronic.

3. Charge Accumulations

As described in chapter 3, static charges may, after the separation, be located on insulators as well as on (insulated) conductors. The physical characteristics as well as the effects of such charge accumulations depend strongly upon which of the two possibilities we are dealing with.

Charges on Insulators

The distribution of charge on an insulator is largely a *local* phenomenon. Let us consider Figure 4.1. The surface charge density σ produced by the charging process around point P_1 is in principle independent of the outcome of the charging at other parts of the body, say around P_2. The charge located on a given area of an insulator is primarily determined by the kind of contact and materials to which

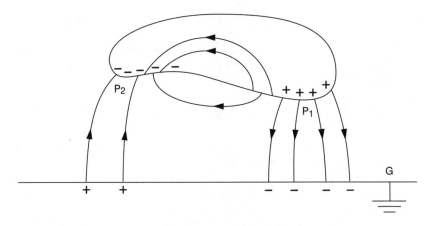

Figure 4.1 Charge distribution on insulator

that particular area has been exposed. The effect of the charge on the surroundings is largely local. At distances large compared to the dimensions of the charged body, or rather of the charged area, the resulting field strength is given by the total charge, i.e., the sum of (positive and negative) charges.

But at close range, the field strength is primarily determined by two other factors: (a) the local surface charge density, and (b) the proximity and shape of nearby grounded conductors.

In Figure 4.2a is shown the surface of a positively charged insulator. Around a point P the surface charge density is σ. In the air immediately in front of P the field strength E is $\leq \sigma/\varepsilon_0$. If a grounded conductor A is brought into the vicinity of P, the field strength in front of A (and especially around sharp points of A) may exceed the breakdown field strength E_b of the air, and a corona or brush discharge may take place between A and the charged surface.

In the discharge positive and negative ions are formed, and (in this case) negative ions are attracted to the charged surface and are partly neutralizing the charge on an area around P (see Figure 4.2b). An equally large, opposite charge is

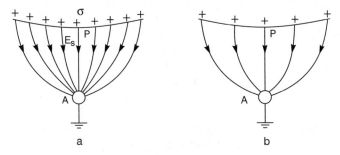

Figure 4.2 Discharge of charged insulator

brought to A by positive ions. It thus appears as if a charge has been transferred from the charged surface to the grounded conductor. The area discharged and the amount of charge transferred vary widely. For strongly charged surfaces, the area may be a few tens of cm^2, and the charge about 10^{-8}–10^{-7} C. Under normal circumstances both quantities may be one or two orders of magnitude smaller.

Incendiveness

During the discharge a certain amount of energy is dissipated in the air where the discharge takes place. It is not possible to measure either the total energy or the distribution of energy over the discharge volume, i.e., the energy density, but experience shows that in general discharges from insulators are much less incendive than discharges and sparks between conductors.

Energies of about 1 mJ have been estimated for strong brush discharges. Thus it is possible to ignite some air-vapor mixtures, but not air-powder mixtures, by brush discharges (see Sections 4 and 5). If the discharge takes the form of a corona discharge no ignition risk exists.

Discharge current

If A is a solid conductor, the charge transferred will pass through A as a current, normally without causing any damage. A may, for instance, be a person, and the discharge will only be sensed as the tickling feeling one experiences when nearing a finger to a piece of charged plastic. But A may also be a semiconductor component or device with one or more terminals grounded. In this case the discharge current may destroy the device or cause latent damage. This is a typical example of the electronic industry's electrostatic discharge (ESD) problem.

Charges on Insulated Conductors

In contrast to the situation with a charged insulator, the distribution of charge on an insulated conductor is an *integral* phenomenon. It has already been explained (Chapter 2, Section 7) that the charge on an insulated conductor will distribute itself over the whole surface of the conductor in such a way that (a) the field strength inside the conductor is zero and thus (b) the voltage with respect to ground of each point of the conductor is the same.

Let us consider an insulated conductor B (see Figure 4.3), characterized by its capacitance C and resistance to ground R. If the charge on the conductor at a given time is q, the voltage is $V = q/C$, and the (decay) current to q ground is $I = q/RC$.

The distribution of charge on and the field strength around the conductor is determined by the capacitance C, but if, for instance, a grounded conductor A is brought into the vicinity of B (see Figure 4.4), the field strength around A may

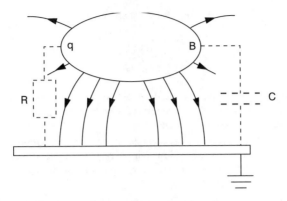

Figure 4.3 Charged insulated conductor

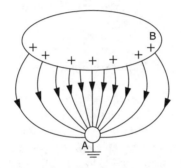

Figure 4.4 Discharge from insulated conductor

exceed the breakdown field strength, in more or less the same way as explained for charged insulators. But the discharge process may evolve very differently in the case of a charged insulated conductor. If either *B* or *A* has sufficiently sharp points the discharge may be a corona or brush discharge, stopping when the field strength at any point no longer exceeds the breakdown field strength, leaving *B* partly but uniformly neutralized. If neither of the conductors has sharp points, the discharge will be a spark (see Chapter 2, Section 10), which will cause an (almost) total neutralization of the charged conductor.

The charge "transferred" and the energy dissipated in corona and brush discharges from charged conductors do not differ much from the same quantities in the case of charged insulators, and consequently their incendiveness and the current pulses through the grounded conductor are also about the same. Spark discharges, on the other hand, differ from corona and brush discharges in three major ways:

(1) A spark discharge will normally neutralize all the charge on the insulated conductor.

(2) The energy W dissipated in the air by a spark, given by

$$W = \frac{1}{2} CV^2$$

may adopt a large range of values, depending on the capacitance C and voltage V of the insulated conductor. As the volume of the discharge channel is very narrow, the energy density of a spark is, for the same total energy dissipated, much higher than for other types of discharges, making sparks generally more explosive. And although there are cases where brush discharges may have tripped an ignition, the cause of most static-induced ignitions or explosions in air-vapor mixtures and air-dust mixtures is a spark discharge.

(3) The current pulse through the conductor A, or any device forming a conductive or semiconductive path from A, to ground may be much faster and stronger than the corresponding pulse caused by any other type of discharge and may consequently be much more destructive.

4. Explosive Mixtures of Vapors and Gases, Ignition Energy

Although there are numerous examples of static electric discharges (almost all of them sparks) having set off explosions or deflagrations, it is conservative to say that most discharges have no noticeable effects, even when they take place in an environment with vapors from liquids like gasoline, ether, and acetone, which sometimes do form explosive mixtures even with atmospheric air. The reason for this is that most discharges do not have enough energy density to start the necessary interactions between enough molecules of the vapor and the oxygen of the air. Or, more precisely, the incidental ratio between the concentrations of the vapor and the oxygen requires more energy dissipated per unit volume than can be delivered by a likely static electric discharge.

This is illustrated in Figure 4.5, which shows the ignition energy for mixtures of ether vapors and pure oxygen or atmospheric air. It appears that it is possible to ignite a mixture of ether vapor and pure oxygen with an energy of a little more than 1 μJ (if the concentration of ether vapor is about 16%), whereas it takes about 0.2 mJ, or about 200 times more energy to ignite a mixture of ether vapor and atmospheric air, and then only if the ether concentration is very close to 6%.

The main reason it takes more energy to ignite a mixture with atmospheric air than with oxygen is that it also takes energy to heat the nitrogen in the air without it participating in the process, and this energy is therefore wasted. It also appears that the necessary ignition energy of ether vapor mixtures increases rapidly if the concentration deviates only slightly from the 6% minimum value. Consequently, only mixtures between maybe 4 and 8% are in practice explosive.

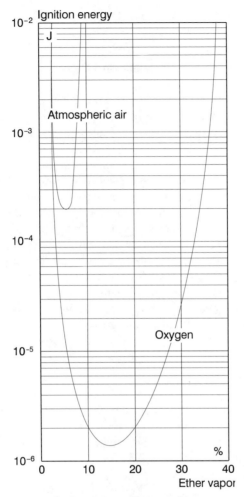

Figure 4.5 Ignition energy of ether vapor mixtures with oxygen and atmospheric air

The curves shown in Figure 4.5 are typical, regarding both shape and energy values, for vapors of many organic compounds, cyclic as well as aliphatic, like hydrocarbons, ketones, etc. The 0.2-mJ value may therefore be taken as a good lower energy limit for vapor-gas mixtures.

Although a spark with the minimum (ignition) energy is potent enough to cause an explosion only in mixtures within a narrow concentration range, it should still be kept in mind that in an open container with the kind of liquid discussed above the concentration of the vapors at the surface of the liquid is far too high for the mixture to be explosive, and at a height of maybe half a meter above the surface the concentration is far too low. Therefore, somewhere in between, the concentration has exactly the critical value, requiring only the minimum energy for the mixture to blow up.

5. Explosive Mixtures of Powders and Gases

It is a well-known fact that explosions may occur not only in vapor-gas mixtures but, under certain conditions, also in clouds of dust or powders. In the 1930s explosions in grain silos were reported at a rate of approximately one per week in the midwestern United States.

As illustrated in Figure 4.5, the (minimum) ignition energy for a vapor-gas mixture is only a question of the nature and concentrations of the vapor and the gas, but the situation is much more complicated for powders. First of all, whereas mixtures of vapors and gases (in closed containers) are normally homogenous with the vapor concentration being the same throughout the whole mixture, the concentration of powder particles in a cloud may easily vary from point to point, making the determination of a minimum ignition energy very difficult. Further, the ignition energy normally depends upon factors like the grain size of the powder involved. However, it generally takes more energy to start an explosion in a cloud of powders than in an explosive vapor-gas mixture. The minimum ignition energies for vapors (in atmospheric air) are lower than 1 mJ, but powders will normally require a minimum of 10 to 100 mJ to combust.

6. Explosion-Safe Voltage

As we have explained, it can be assumed that any electrical discharge disseminating less than 0.2 mJ in the atmosphere is not incendive. For a capacitive system with a typical capacitance of, say 300 pF, this means that an "explosion-safe" voltage, V_{es}, according to equation (2.33), is

$$V_{es} = \sqrt{\frac{2W_{min}}{C}} = \sqrt{\frac{2 \cdot 0.2 \cdot 10^{-3}}{300 \cdot 10^{-12}}} \simeq 1100\text{--}1200 \text{ V} \qquad (4.1)$$

It should be stressed that this safe-voltage level refers only to explosion risks. When dealing with electronic ESD problems, the acceptable levels are often considerably lower. Also, as mentioned before, the safe-voltage level only applies to insulated conductors, as voltage cannot (or hardly ever) be meaningfully determined for an insulating material.

7. Voltage Level of Charged Conductors

Most static electric effects of a charged insulated conductor, i.e., a capacitive system, are determined by the voltage of the system. Such a system, electrically characterized by its capacitance C and (decay) resistance to ground R, may attain its voltage in two distinctly different ways: by *bulk charging* or by *current charging*.

Bulk Charging

If a charge q is transferred to the (uncharged) system in a time short compared to the time constant of the system $\tau = RC$, the voltage will almost instantaneously rise to an initial voltage V_0 given by

$$V_0 = \frac{q_0}{C}$$

A decay current I with the initial value

$$I_0 = \frac{V_0}{R}$$

will start to flow, making the charge q and voltage V of the conductor decrease with time according to the formulas

$$q = q_0 \exp\left(-\frac{t}{\tau}\right)$$

and

$$V = V_0 \exp\left(-\frac{t}{\tau}\right) \tag{4.2}$$

The initial electrostatic energy stored in the system is

$$W_0 = \frac{1}{2} CV_0^2$$

The energy will decrease with time as

$$W = W_0 \exp\left(-\frac{2t}{\tau}\right) \tag{4.3}$$

This kind of charging may happen if, for instance, a piece of charged insulating material is dumped into an insulated conducting container. The charged insulating material may in itself offer no static electric risk, but once the charge is transferred to the capacitive system (maybe only by induction), the situation may, as explained before, be entirely different. It is generally not possible to put an upper limit on the initial voltage reached by a capacitive system by bulk charging.

EXAMPLE 4.1:

A sheet of plastic with a total charge $q = 3 \cdot 10^{-7}$ C is placed in an uncharged, insulated container with a capacitance $C = 200$ pF and a resistance to ground $R = 10^{11}$ Ω. The initial voltage of the container will be

$$V_0 = \frac{q_0}{C} = \frac{3 \cdot 10^{-7}}{200 \cdot 10^{-12}} = 1500 \text{ V}$$

The energy stored in the system is

$$W_0 = \frac{1}{2} CV^2 = \frac{1}{2} \cdot 200 \cdot 10^{-12} \cdot 1500^2 = 0.2 \text{ mJ}$$

If no discharge takes place from the system, after a time $\tau = RC = 10^{11} \cdot 200 \cdot 10^{-12} = 20$ s, the voltage will have dropped to

$$V = \frac{1}{e} V_0 \simeq 550 \text{ V}$$

and the energy to

$$W = \frac{1}{e^2} W_0 \simeq 0.03 \text{ mJ}$$

The energy "lost" has been dissipated as heat in the ground resistance.

Current Charging

With many static charging processes the charge is transferred to the system as a more or less steady charging current I_c. This may, for instance, be the case when an insulated container is being filled with a charged liquid or powder or, with some approximation, when a person is walking across an insulating floor covering. The current I_c will bring a charge to the system and cause the voltage to increase. But this, on the other hand, will produce an increasing decay current I_d, i.e., a flow of charge from the system to ground, until the two currents cancel each other and an equilibrium maximum voltage V_m is reached.

The rate of net increase of the charge q at a time t after the start of charging is given by

$$\frac{dq}{dt} = I_c - I_d = I_c - \frac{V}{R} = I_c - \frac{q}{RC} \tag{4.4}$$

where V is the voltage at time t. The solution to equation (4.4) is

$$q = RCI_c \left[1 - \exp\left(-\frac{t}{\tau}\right) \right] \tag{4.5}$$

where $\tau = RC$, and correspondingly for the voltage

$$V = RI_c\left[1 - \exp\left(-\frac{t}{\tau}\right)\right] \tag{4.6}$$

The equilibrium maximum voltage V is thus given by

$$V_m = RI_c \tag{4.7}$$

EXAMPLE 4.2:

Gasoline is being pumped into an insulated container at a rate of $u = 10$ liters per second (10^{-2} m$^3 \cdot$ s^{-1}), see Chapter 3, Figure 3.4. The gasoline is electrically charged with a volume charge density $\rho = 10^{-5}$ C $\cdot$ m^{-3}. The container has a capacitance $C = 200$ pF and a resistance to ground $R = 10^{11}$ Ω. The flow of gasoline will produce a charging current

$$I_c = \rho u = 10^{-5} \cdot 10^{-2} = 10^{-7} \text{ A}$$

If the container is originally uncharged, the voltage V of the container will increase with a time constant

$$\tau = RC = 10^{11} \cdot 200 \cdot 10^{-12} = 20 \text{ s}$$

according to

$$V = RI_c\left[1 - \exp\left(-\frac{t}{\tau}\right)\right] = 10^{11} \cdot 10^{-7}\left[1 - \exp\left(-\frac{t}{20}\right)\right]$$

$$= 10^4\left[1 - \exp\left(-\frac{t}{20}\right)\right]$$

with an equilibrium maximum voltage of

$$V_m = 10^4 \text{ V}$$

The voltage will have reached a value of

$$V = 10^4\,[1 - \exp(-1)] = 6300 \text{ V}$$

at a time $t = \tau = 20$ s after start of filling. The energy stored in the system at this time is

$$W = \frac{1}{2}CV^2 = \frac{1}{2} \cdot 200 \cdot 10^{-12} \cdot 6300^2 \approx 4 \text{ mJ}$$

Charging of a person by walking

A special case of current charging is that of a person walking across an insulating floor covering wearing shoes with insulating soles. The person can be considered as a capacitive system with a capacitance $C \approx 200$ pF (likely range 100–400 pF) and a decay resistance to ground R ranging anywhere from a few MΩ (if the floor is to be considered insulating at all) to 10^{15} Ω or more. The contact and friction between soles and floor will separate electric charges that, being transferred to the person, will make her voltage increase.

The actual process is rather complicated to describe in detail, but the following model gives a fairly good idea of the influence of the relevant parameters. At each step a charge Δq is being separated and transferred to the capacitance C. If the number of steps per unit time is n, the charging current I_c is given by

$$I_c = n\Delta q \qquad (4.8)$$

and according to equation (4.7) the maximum voltage to be reached by the person is

$$V_c = Rn\Delta q \qquad (4.9)$$

EXAMPLE 4.3:

A person with a capacitance $C = 200$ pF is walking across an insulating floor with a step rate of $n = 2$ s^{-1} (ISO standard step rate for testing of floor coverings). The charge being transferred to the person at each step is $\Delta q = 5 \cdot 10^{-8}$ C. The decay resistance of the person to ground is $R = 10^{11}$ Ω. The maximum voltage of the person can be calculated to be

$$V_m = Rn\Delta q = 10^{11} \cdot 2 \cdot 5 \cdot 10^{-8} = 10^4 \text{ V}$$

Although the value calculated from equation (4.9) undoubtedly gives the upper value for the body voltage, this simple calculation does not always adequately describe actual charging conditions.

In Figure 4.6 is shown a recording of the body voltage as a function of time for the case considered in Example 4.3. The floor covering was nylon needle felt and the shoe soles leather, and as a result the body voltage was negative. The resistance R was measured from the person's hand to ground, and the steady-state value varied over the walking area from $0.5 \cdot 10^{11}$ to $1.5 \cdot 10^{11}$ Ω. The step rate was close to 2 steps per second. The charge separated per step, $\Delta q = 5 \cdot 10^{-8}$ C, was measured separately, and the value given is the average for 20 steps.

It appears that the increase in voltage is not smooth as suggested in equation (4.6), but occurs in jerks corresponding to the separation and contact between soles and floor covering. When a foot is lifted from the floor, the voltage increases not only because the body charge increases, but also because the capacitance momentarily decreases (distance between one set of capacitor plates increases). When the foot is brought down again, the voltage decreases, not because the charge decreases, but because the capacitance regains its rest value (two feet value).

The maximum body voltage is about 3 kV, or one-third of the theoretical value from Example 4.3. The explanation of this lower value can be deduced from Figure 4.7, which shows the body voltage as a function of time after a person has stopped walking and is standing still.

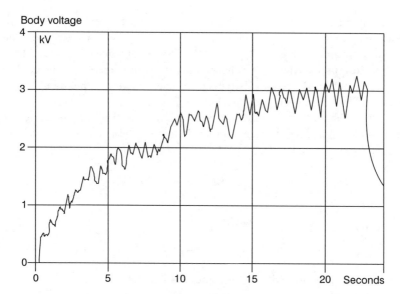

Figure 4.6 Body voltage of person walking across insulating floor

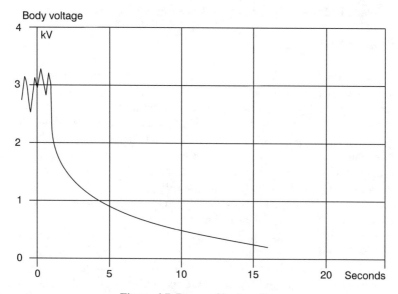

Figure 4.7 Decay of body voltage

According to equation (4.2), the voltage should be expected to decrease exponentially with time with a time constant $\tau = RC = 10^{11} \cdot 200 \cdot 10^{-12} = 20$ s, but an analysis of the curve discloses that the decay is not strictly exponential. The initial slope of the curve corresponding to a time constant $\tau_i \approx 4$ s gradually changes to a constant final value $\tau_f \approx 18$ s after about 5 seconds. With a body capacitance of $C = 200$ pF, this indicates that the effective decay resistance changes from an initial value $R_i \approx 2 \cdot 10^{10}\ \Omega$ to a final value of $R_f \approx 9 \cdot 10^{10}\ \Omega$. This increase in resistance (or rather resistivity) with decreasing voltage difference (or better, field strength) is typical for many materials, including those of which resistors are made.

If it is assumed that the effective resistance during the charging experiment (see Figure 4.6) lies somewhere between R_i and R_f, the maximum body voltage should lie somewhere between

$$V_i = R_i n \Delta q = 2 \cdot 10^{10} \cdot 2 \cdot 0.5 \cdot 10^{-7} = 2\ \text{kV} \qquad (4.10)$$

and

$$V_f = R_f n \Delta q = 9 \cdot 10^{10} \cdot 2 \cdot 0.5 \cdot 10^{-7} = 9\ \text{kV} \qquad (4.11)$$

in good correspondence with the measured value of 3 kV.

8. Current Pulses from Charged Systems

ESD Damage Models

The decay of body voltage shown in Figure 4.7 is an example of a weak current pulse from a charged capacitive system, in this case a person charged to 3 kV, her charge leaking slowly away, starting with a current of 0.1–0.2 μA, which slows down to a few nA in 20 seconds. This kind of current pulse is not felt by the person participating in the process, and the pulse would hardly be capable of affecting any kind of system, electronic or otherwise, if the conditions were so that the pulse could pass through such a system.

The situation is completely different, however, if a charged capacitive system is suddenly being decharged, for instance by being connected through a relatively low resistance to a sensitive device, kept at ground potential.

It is obviously very important to be able to test the sensitivity of electronic and other devices for the kind of current pulses originating from such discharges, for instance, from a charged person. Such testing could of course, in principle, be done by using a live, charged person, but for obvious reasons it is more practical to utilize an electrical circuit that simulates the (electrical) behavior of the charged system. Over the past 20 years several models have been developed to simulate the discharge from various types of charged systems, which possibly might be destructive to sensitive devices. The primary models are *the human body model (HBM), the machine model (MM), and the charged device model (CDM).*

Human Body Model

In certain situations an insulated person is electrically adequately represented by a capacitance C ($\approx$ 100–400 pF) in parallel with a (ground) resistance R, which may have values from a few hundred ohms to a petaohm or even more. This is the situation for a freestanding person (Figure 4.8).

If the person is charged, the major part of the charge is located on those areas of her body where the distance to grounded surroundings is the shortest, which in practice means on the soles of her feet. Actually the distance in question is the **dielectric distance**, i.e., the geometrical distance divided by the relative permittivity of the interdistance material, and as the permittivity of the shoe soles plus floor covering is normally 2–5 times that of atmospheric air, this makes the soles of the feet an even more predestined charge location.

EXAMPLE 4.4:

Let us assume that the person from Figure 4.8, with a capacitance C = 200 pF and a decay ground resistance R = 10^{11} Ω, is charged to a voltage V = 3 kV. The charge on the person is

$$q = CV = 200 \cdot 10^{-12} \cdot 3000 = 6 \cdot 10^{-7} \, \text{C}$$

Of this charge maybe 30% or $\approx 2 \cdot 10^{-7}$ C is distributed unevenly over her body, whereas the major part of the charge ($\approx 4 \cdot 10^{-7}$ C) is located on the underside of her feet.

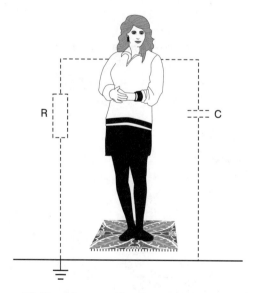

Figure 4.8 Capacitance and resistance of standing person

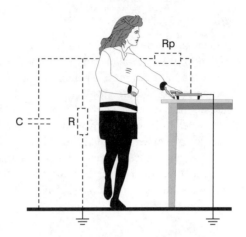

Figure 4.9 Human body discharge

All points of the freestanding person have the same voltage V, and the field strength inside the person and along her skin is zero.

If now the person touches a grounded device (see Figure 4.9), the point of contact, often the tip of a finger, is brought to ground potential, and a field is established in and on the body, causing the charges to flow from their equilibrium location to the point of contact through an average body resistance R_p of 1 to 2 kΩ. The resulting current pulse, however, is not adequately described by a simple exponential function as in equation (4.2), nor even by a simple monotonous decay with an increasing time constant as in Figure 4.7.

The current will start at zero and rise to a peak value I_p within maybe 10 ns, after which it will decay with a time constant of some hundred ns. (See Figure 4.10.) The

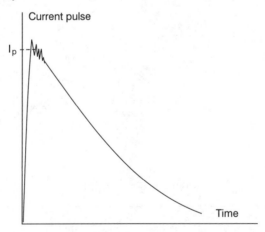

Figure 4.10 Current pulse from charged person

peak value of the pulse may easily have a magnitude of several amperes, and there will normally be some oscillations in the initial part of the decay.

The time constant for the pulse $\tau = R_p C$ obviously depends on the individual values of R_p and C, and it is interesting to note that over the years there has been quite some uncertainty regarding the likely range of values for R_p as well as C. For test purposes, R_p is now usually chosen as 1.5 kΩ and the test circuit is designed to give a pulse with rise and decay times as suggested above.

Other Models

The **machine model (MM)** simply consists of a capacitor of 200 pF and therefore differs from the HBM mainly by having no series resistor. The MM represents charged insulated conductors like metallic containers, vehicles, and conductive tote boxes. The peak current in an MM discharge may be much larger than in an HBM discharge.

The **charged device model (CDM)** deals with the effect on a component or device from decay of charges on the part itself, where the charging can be caused by contact and friction between the part and insulating package material. The model applies to any device that has a capacitance to ground and is characterized by this capacitance, the inductance of the leads, and the resistance of the discharge path. The discharge will be a damped oscillation with a period of maybe 1 ns, and although the total charge on a device may only be of the order of nC, the amplitude of the current may be several amperes.

The **field-induced model (FIM)** describes the inductive (see Chapter 2, Section 4) effect of an electric field on a device or insulated conductor. Other models are the **capacitive-coupled model (CCM)**, the **floating-device model**, and the **transient-induced model**. For more details on all the models, the reader is referred to the literature, for instance, Owen J. McAteer, *Electrostatic Discharge Control*, McGraw-Hill, New York, 1990.

Chapter 5

Abatement of Static Electricity

to reduce in degree or intensity

Although useful applications of static electric effects are numerous, in most peoples' minds, static electric phenomena are harmful, and their effects should be avoided and abated. The most fundamental way of doing this would be to prevent charges from being separated, and in situations where friction between two solid materials is essential for the charging, a reduction of the degree of friction will of course reduce the charges separated. In the case of charging by flow of insulating liquids, a reduction of the flow rate will likewise reduce the charges separated. Also, because spraying of almost any kind of liquid often results in charge separation, free jets of liquids should be avoided whenever possible, for instance, by keeping the flow rate low when filling containers, until the tip of the filling tube is immersed in the liquid.

But these are probably also the only cases in which the actual magnitude of the charges separated can be affected, although certain treatments or procedures are claimed to reduce or remove static electric problems by reducing the charging. However, it is likely that the efficiency of most of these methods depends on an improved neutralization or recombination of the charges separated, rather than on an actual reduction of the charging rate.

1. Grounding of Conductors

The basic rule of fighting static electricity is to ground all conductors that might possibly become charged or exposed to induction from other charged objects. Insulated charged conductors can produce energetic spark discharges, but even if the atmosphere contains no explosive mixtures, it is important to discharge conductive systems in order to avoid other bothersome effects of static charge buildup.

The grounding must include all conducting objects, not only machinery and main structures, but also each part of any piping or tubing system, containers, and fixed and moving parts. A literal, direct, connection to ground is in principle not necessary, as long as all conducting parts are interconnected, so that no voltage differences occur (bonding). It should also be mentioned that a bolting of flanges in a tubing system does not necessarily ensure sufficient contact between the individual parts of the system, as paint, rust, and grease may create insulating layers. An efficient connection can be established by the use of special wire loops, soldered or screwed onto the tubes, across the couplings.

Containers may become charged during filling with liquids or powders. If such a container is placed on a concrete floor that is kept wet, this will normally ensure a sufficiently low resistance to ground. As a general rule, however, receiving containers should be connected with the (grounded) filling system before filling starts. This is especially important when handling liquids, like gasoline and acetone, whose vapors may form explosive mixtures with the air.

Tank trucks should be connected with a special ground wire to the storage tank structure, during filling as well as emptying. This should be done even though the tires are normally made of carbon-loaded (semi)conductive rubber (see page 81). Although the conductivity of such tires is high enough to prevent dangerous charge buildup on the truck during driving, the charge separation caused by the flow of the gasoline may be so fast that the leakage through the tires is insufficient to keep the voltage of the truck at a safe level, especially if the ground is dry.

But even when handling relatively small volumes, like a few gallons, of volatile liquids, suitable grounding procedures for all conducting items should be strictly followed. Apart from the basic rule of interconnecting storage and receiving containers, it is also important to connect any kind of conductors, like filling heads, anywhere in the flow system to either end of the flow line. Also, nongrounded (conducting) devices like level gauges or more incidental items, like metal cans floating on the surface of the liquid, should be avoided. The charge separation by flow of insulating liquids can also be reduced by adding antistatic additives to the liquids.

2. Methods of Grounding Persons

In static electric context, human beings are to be considered as conductors. Because of the insulating properties of footwear and floor coverings, a person often constitutes a capacitive system (Chapter 2, Section 16), with her own capacitance in the range of a few hundred pF and with a leakage resistance ranging from almost zero to maybe 10^{14}–10^{15} Ω or more. The problem of persons and static electricity has to be looked at from two different points of view. One deals with the way in which static electric charging may bother a charged person, e.g., the nuisance of electric shocks when touching the banisters or elevator button or kissing one's spouse, the induction of rashes and eczemae by field-induced plateout of airborne allergens on the skin, or even the questionable effects of inhaling fewer or more air ions when charged. These problems are discussed in Chapter 7, Section 2.

From the other point of view, a person is just another conductor who, in certain environments, may pose a hazard as long as she is insulated, and who therefore has to be (virtually) grounded in a safe, practical manner.

Footwear and Floor Coverings

In many cases the static electric problem connected with a charged person is that a possible spark discharge from the person constitutes an ignition hazard when explosive vapor-air mixtures may be present in the working environment. Up until the 1970s this was a real concern in hospital operating rooms, because of the common use of anaesthetics like diethyl ether and especially cyclopropane. The risk was counteracted by the installation of floors made conductive often by mixing carbon black into the matrix of the normally inorganic (ceramic) floor materials and by the use of footwear with soles made totally or in part of conductive rubber, which was also used extensively for anaesthetic tubing, wheels on operating tool carts, stool supports, etc. As the use of volatile anaesthetics forming explosive vapor-air mixtures rapidly decreased, so did the risk of static-caused accidents in hospitals, but the risk obviously remains in any environment where organic solvents are handled.

As already stated, any conducting item should be properly grounded (or bonded), and consequently so should all personnel. The requirements, however, on the value of the grounding resistance depend strongly upon whether the person is being charged only by walking on an insulating floor covering, or whether the person may also receive charges, e.g., by holding a sack or other type of container from which a powder or a liquid is being poured.

If we only consider charging by walking, it is easy to estimate an acceptable upper limit for the grounding (or decay) resistance for the person. From equation (4.9), if a body voltage V_m can be tolerated, the maximum acceptable grounding resistance R_m is given by

$$R_m = \frac{V_m}{n \Delta q} \tag{5.1}$$

The maximum permissible value V_m of the body voltage depends upon the working environment. If, for instance, the atmosphere contains explosive mixtures of vapors with known minimum ignition energy W_{min}, V_m has to be smaller than the explosion-safe voltage V_{es} calculated from equation (4.1).

EXAMPLE 5.1:

A person with a capacitance $C = 200$ pF is walking across a floor with a step rate $n = 2 \text{ s}^{-1}$. The charge transferred to the person at each step is $\Delta q = 5 \cdot 10^{-8}$ C.

The atmosphere contains ether vapors in a mixture with a minimum ignition energy $W_{min} = 0.2$ mJ. Equation (4.1) yields

$$V_{es} = \sqrt{\frac{2W_{min}}{C}} = \sqrt{\frac{2 \cdot 0.2 \cdot 10^{-3}}{200 \cdot 10^{-12}}} = 1300\text{--}1400 \text{ V}$$

If V_m thus is chosen as 1000 V, equation (5.1) leads to a maximum grounding resistance of

$$R_m = \frac{V_m}{n\Delta q} = \frac{1000}{2 \cdot 5 \cdot 10^{-8}} = 10^{10} \; \Omega$$

Example 5.1 indicates that it often does not require a literal (metal) ground wire for an object to be kept at a low potential. In practice, however, a maximum grounding resistance as high as that calculated in Example 5.1 would not be recommended.

Normally a maximum value of 10–100 MΩ for the floor itself and 0.5–1 MΩ for the shoes are suggested. Values as low as these will also ensure that most other charging sources in addition to walking do not lead to dangerous body voltages.

Often a lower limit for the grounding resistance (from 250 kΩ–1 MΩ) is also required. Part of the logic of such a requirement has been the risk of personnel touching live wires while being too effectively grounded through the footwear and floor covering. The extra safety obtained by this precaution does, however, seem somewhat marginal and even false considering the variety of permanently grounded objects that a person might accidentally or unknowingly contact.

As stated above, for many years the major concern about static electric risks was that of discharges, mostly sparks, causing ignitions in inflammable atmospheres. Although this is still a real and serious risk in certain areas, over the past two decades the emphasis in abating static electric charge accumulations has moved to the electronic environment. Computers and printers may fail if a person, charged to a voltage as low as 1000–2000 V, is discharging herself to some grounded item in the immediate vicinity of such electronic equipment. This problem is obviously solved by fulfilling the same kind of grounding requirements of personnel through footwear and floor coverings as outlined above for environments where explosive vapor mixtures may be present.

Wrist Straps

For more sensitive items, like metal oxide semiconductor field effect transistors (MOSFETs), where a current pulse from a person charged to 100 V or less can be destructive, the previously described simple grounding procedures may prove inadequate. Although the idea of keeping a person at zero voltage by literally tying him physically to a point at ground potential by a conducting wire may seem odd and impractical to many people, this is nevertheless the preferred and accepted procedure in many areas of the electronic world.

The gadget employed for this purpose, called a **wrist strap**, consists of a band or chain made of metal, like an expandable watchband, and conductive plastic or conductive fibers, connected to ground by a strap, either made of solid conductive plastic or of multistrand wire. Normally the strap includes a series safety resistor of 1 MΩ for minimizing the shock from accidentally touching a live wire while being tied to ground via the strap. For the normal household peak voltage of 310 V AC (220 V effective), the maximum current through the person would then be 0.31 μA, well below fatal values.

Even though wrist straps seem simple enough devices to employ, their use does involve a series of problems to be considered, like intermittent skin contact with loose-fitting bands, bad skin contact caused by excessively dry skin or too much body hair, or sluffing of the band material, resulting in contamination of electronic components. Also, the actual grounding of the strap should be done carefully to a separate ground terminal and not be left to a chance connection through an alligator clip hooked onto some "suitable" point.

3. Neutralizing Charges on Insulators

Although discharges from charged insulating surfaces are usually less energetic, and thus less incendive or otherwise destructive, than the spark-type discharges from conductors, there are numerous examples of charged insulators causing ignitions of explosive vapor-air mixtures, attracting dust to exposed surfaces, and, probably most impoprtantly, inducing destructive ESD events.

It is therefore of importance to be able to neutralize charges located on insulating materials. This can, in principle, be done in three different ways: by conductance through the bulk of the material, conductance along the surface of the material, or by the use of oppositely charged ions from the surrounding air. These methods are described in the following sections.

Bulk-Conductive Insulators

Basically, it is self-contradictory to talk about transporting charges through an insulator. If this is possible, the material is not really insulating. Over the years many attempts have been made to give insulating materials a suitable conductivity, without ruining their other (usually mechanical) desirable properties. Normally this is done by mixing the material with inherently conductive additives. The best-known example of such an intrinsic antistatic agent is carbon black. Carbon black can be added to a variety of polymeric materials and is used where the resulting blackening of the base material is acceptable. For many years the most important area of use has been that of manufacturing conductive rubber.

Ordinary vulcanized rubber may have a bulk resistivity of 10^{13} $\Omega \cdot$ m, but adding carbon black may lower the resistivity by a factor of up to 10^{15}. Normally, however, a resistivity of about 10^5–10^6 $\Omega \cdot$ m will be low enough to prevent dangerous or annoying charge accumulations. Conductive rubber is used extensively in hospital operating rooms, in tubing for anaesthetic machines, for wheels on tool carts, as parts of soles of antistatic footwear, and in many other ways. Another important use of conductive rubber is in the manufacturing of car tires. It was actually the need for antistatic tires that led to the development of conductive rubber.

In the middle thirties two new aspects of Western civilization brought the nuisance of static electricity to the attention of the general population, at least in the United States. One was the appearance of car radios. The quality of reception of often distant AM stations could be severely impeded by the crackling caused by discharges from the car, charged by the rolling friction between the tires and the road surface. The other innovation was the introduction of toll roads. When the unsuspecting driver handed over his nickel to the toll collector, both parties might experience an unplesant shock. With the development of conductive or antistatic tires, all this became history.

If the road surface is not excessively dry and insulating, a car will not be charged. Nevertheless, many drivers, at least in Europe, equip their cars with trailing conductive tails to bleed away static charges that the tires have already taken care of. And even if the surface conditions in exceptional cases do lead to a charging of the car, the tail will not remedy this problem.

The reason for this unnecessary double precaution is probably an understandable misunderstanding. The shock many a driver (or passenger) experiences when getting out of a car is not caused by discharging the car to ground. What happens is that the driver may become charged when sliding over the seat cover, in the same way that one may become charged when getting up from a chair with an insulating seat. As a result, a spark may jump from the person to any metal part of the car, which is virtually at ground potential.

Returning to the subject of carbon black, another use is in the manufacturing of fibers for textile floor coverings. The fibers may be made with either a central core of carbon black and a sheath of, for instance, polyamide, or conversely, with a polyamide fiber central core and a carbon black sheath. When such combination fibers are mixed with ordinary, highly insulating fibers, in a ratio of a few percent, the result is a material that rarely produces substantial chargings.

But at least economically, the most important use of carbon black is no doubt in the electronics industry. By loading the base materials for carrier trays, holders, tubes, boxes, bags, etc., with carbon black, these items are made sufficiently conductive to ensure a rapid neutralization of static charges on the material itself. Usually the loading is done uniformly throughout the matrix of the material, increasing the bulk conductivity, but it may also take the form of a thin surface conductive layer.

Surface-Conductive Insulators

It is well known that static electric problems seldom occur in environments with relatively high air humidity, say above 50–60%. This fact has sometimes been erroneously interpreted as humid air being more conductive than dry air, but this is not the case. If anything, humid air is less conductive, as the mobility of small air ions decreases slightly with increasing air humidity. The effect of increased air humidity is to increase the thickness of the moisture layer present on (and possibly in) all surfaces, which will provide a sufficiently conductive path for charges to leak away. The amount of water vapor adsorbed or absorbed from the air is strongly dependent on the materials in question. At humidities as low as 30–35%, a material like cotton may show little charge retention, whereas a material like nylon may require humidities of 50% or more before it can be considered antistatic. Generally speaking, no resulting charges appear at humidities of 60% or higher. Humidities at such high levels, on the other hand, will often pose practical, technical, or hygienic problems, if they are to be maintained over extended periods.

Antistatic agents, topical antistats

It is often possible to render highly insulative materials sufficiently surface conductive, even at relatively low humidities, by treating the surface with antistatic agents, commonly known as **topical antistats**. These agents function by forming a thin layer (a few molecules thick) on the surface, and this layer will attract moisture from the air much more readily than will an untreated surface.

Antistatic agents obviously have to be hygroscopic, but it is further required that they have a low vapor pressure in order not to evaporate too fast from the surfaces treated. Further requirements concern color, toxicity, inflammability, etc. Chemically speaking, antistatic agents are amphipathic compounds, their molecules containing a hydrophobic group to which is attached a hydrophilic end group. According to the nature of the end group, the agents are divided into cationic, anionic, and nonionogenic agents. Cationic materials are usually high-molecular quaternary ammonium halogenides or ethoxylated fatty amines or amides; anionic materials may be sulfonated hydrocarbons, and nonionogenic materials polyalkylene oxide esters.

Topical antistats are used extensively in the textile, plastic, printing, and many other industries. A very common use is the treatment of floor coverings to reduce the level of body voltage of persons walking across the floor. With textile floor coverings, a proper antistatic treatment may work for two to three months. With hard floor coverings, the antistatic treatment normally has to be repeated after each washing.

Permanently antistatic materials

In some cases antistatic agents may be compounded with a polymer, either before the polymerization or at least before extrusion. The best-known example of this technique is probably the manufacture of antistatic polyethylene, commonly known as **pink poly**, originally developed by the late Dan Anderson of ESD fame.

Ethoxylated fatty amines or amides are mixed with a resin, like low-density polyethylene, and an antiblock, like calcium carbonate (to prevent stickiness). After extrusion or moulding to the required end product (film, sheets, trays, boxes, etc.), the additive has to diffuse ("bloom") to the surface in order to be able to attract moisture from the air and thus render the material antistatic.

Pink poly, which may appear in a variety of colors besides pink, is no doubt the most widely used material in the electronic industry for packaging, storing, and transporting of sensitive components and circuits. Materials with built-in additives, like pink poly, will maintain their antistatic properties as long as the additive is present on the surface. Although the vapor pressure of most additives is fairly low, a certain evaporation of additive is always taking place from the surface. For fresh materials this evaporation is more or less counterbalanced by a diffusion of additive from the interior of the material. As the supply of additive in the solid is depleted, the surface concentration cannot be maintained. The surface is said to "dry out," the surface resistivity will increase, and the material will eventually lose its antistatic properties. The effective lifetime of a permanently antistatic material depends upon a variety of factors, the most important of which are the temperature of the environment and the thickness of the material, which (for a given volume concentration) determines the amount of additive available for diffusion to the surface. It should also be mentioned that the additive diffusing to the surface, besides attracting moisture from the air, may react in an unwanted way with components and devices coming into contact with the material. Examples of this are PCBs and other items made of polycarbonate being crazed and cracking when packed in antistatic materials containing fatty amines.

4. Charge Neutralization by Air Ions

All the methods discussed previously for "removing" (neutralizing) charges on insulators are based on some kind of modification of bulk or surface properties of the insulative material. However, often such modifications are not feasible or acceptable. In these cases only one method remains: neutralizing the charges by oppositely charged air ions. The nature of air ions, or atmospheric ions, is briefly discussed in Chapter 2, Section 17, and the mechanism of charge neutralization by air ions is explained in the sections Charge Decay Through the Air, I and II. Before discussing the specific problems or advantages of using air ions, a short survey of the various types of ionizers and ionizing systems will be given.

Ionizers

Although the nature and composition of air ions may vary with time, space, and production method, any ionization process in air starts with the removal of an electron from a neutral molecule. The necessary energy may be delivered to the molecule from a colliding particle or from a quantum of electromagnetic radiation energy. Only two ionization methods are in practical technical use: *radioactive ionization* and *field ionization*.

Radioactive ionization

Alpha particles are emitted from a decaying radioactive atom with energies on the order of 4–8 MeV (≈ 6–$13 \cdot 10^{-13}$ J). On its way through the air an alpha particle will knock off electrons from neutral air molecules (see Figure 5.1) at the expense of about 34 eV for each successful collision. After having traveled a distance of 2–7 cm, the alpha particle has lost its energy (and velocity) and produced about 200,000 ion pairs along its track.

Field ionization

If air is exposed to an electric field, ions (created by natural radiation) will move in the field and collide with (neutral) molecules after having traveled the mean free path characteristic for the ions. One might expect such collisions to cause ionization in much the same way as collisions between alpha particles and molecules. But even at the highest possible field strengths, the energy of the ions at the end of their mean free path is not high enough to release an electron.

The electrons, on the other hand, freed by the natural radioactive ionization, will also move under the action of the field. Although, over the same distance,

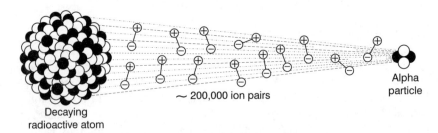

Figure 5.1 Ionization by alpha radiation

they receive the same energy as any other particle carrying an elementary charge, the mean free path for an electron is so much longer that, when exposed to an electric field of about $3 \cdot 10^6$ V $\cdot$ m^{-1} (with plane electrodes and at atmospheric pressure), the electron is able to ionize molecules of the air. The electron, subsequently being freed, will also be accelerated to ionize in the whole region where the field strength is high enough.

Controlled field ionization, in contrast to random discharges, is normally achieved by creating the necessary high field strength in front of a set of conducting electrodes in the form of sharp points or thin wires, by keeping the electrodes at a high potential ($\approx$ 2–20 kV) with respect to some suitable counter electrode, which may even be the walls of the room. The breakdown field strength E_b has the values

$$\text{for points} \quad E_b \simeq \left(300 + \frac{18}{\sqrt{r}}\right) \cdot 10^4 \text{ V} \cdot \text{m}^{-1} \tag{5.2}$$

$$\text{for wires} \quad E_b \simeq \left(300 + \frac{9}{\sqrt{r}}\right) \cdot 10^4 \text{ V} \cdot \text{m}^{-1} \tag{5.3}$$

where r is the radius of the points and wires, respectively (in meters).

It appears that the breakdown field given by equations (5.2) and (5.3) is higher than for a parallel electrode system, but because the field will be strongly inhomogeneous at a sharp electrode (see Figure 5.2), the necessary voltage is much lower than would be the case with parallel plates. Equations (5.2) and (5.3) are only approximately valid. Also, the discharge conditions (for points) are different for positive and negative voltages. The positive voltage necessary to start ionization under given geometrical conditions is about 30% higher than the corresponding negative voltage.

It should be emphasized that it is a (high) field strength, and not a high voltage, that causes ionization. If an ionizing electrode is placed, say 10 mm, from a

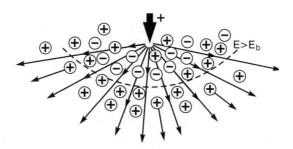

Figure 5.2 Electric field ionization

grounded conductor, an electrode voltage of 2 kV may be enough to cause ionization, whereas 5–6 kV may be required if the nearest grounded object is some meters away. In both cases the field around the electrode will be more or less the same, and the breakdown field strength E_b will be exceeded in a region of maybe a few mm from the electrode. Only in this region does ionization take place, and the ions, always formed in pairs of positive and negative in equal numbers, are separated. If the voltage of the electrode is positive, the negative ions will move to the electrode and become neutralized, and the positive ions will be repelled and move away from the electrode, possibly aided by an air current. Because the field strength will decrease with the distance from the electrode, the velocity of the ions moving away will, according to equation (2.34), also decrease, from initial values of about 100 m · s^{-1} to maybe 1–2 cm · s^{-1} at the walls of the room, if the ions ever get that far before being neutralized.

Emitters do not emit ions

An electrode in an ionizing device is often called an *emitter*, but it is important to note that the electrode does not actually *emit* ions. The ions are created by the *field* immediately in front of the emitter, and the apparently emitted ions (positive in Figure 5.2) have never been in contact with the emitter. Actually the emitter *receives* ions (negative in Figure 5.2). When these ions have been neutralized at the emitter they cease to exist as ions and turn once more into air and water molecules.

If an ammeter is inserted in series with the electrode a current may be measured. This **ionization** or **corona current** is the current it takes to neutralize the ions arriving at the emitter. Under steady-state conditions it has the same magnitude as, but is not identical to, the current of ions moving away. If the corona current is used as a measure of the output of ions from the ionizing device to the surrounding air, it should be kept in mind that often a (substantial) fraction of the ions emitted plate out on more or less grounded parts of the ionizer or on neighboring surfaces without ever reaching those regions where their neutralizing (or other) effects are wanted.

Types of Ionizers

Ionizer bars

Ionizers for neutralizing static charges were first put to practical use in the textile, printing, and (somewhat later) plastic industries. In most cases these ionizers were bar shaped and mounted parallel with and at a short distance from charged sheets of material.

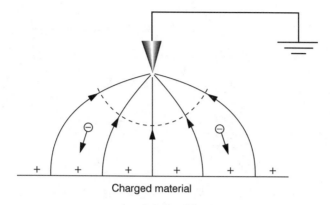

Charged material

Figure 5.3 Passive ionizer

Passive ionizer

The simplest of all ionizing devices is the **passive ionizer**, which consists of one or more grounded thin wires, or more often a row of grounded conductive, sharp points placed a few centimeters from the charged material (see Figure 5.3).

The field from the charge will be deformed by the points and may in a small region in front of the points exceed the breakdown field, as given by equation (5.2) or (5.3), resulting in a corona discharge. Ions of opposite polarity will move towards the charged material and partly neutralize its charge. It is interesting to note that the electrode at which the ionization takes place is at ground potential. But the field strength in front of the electrode may still be high. Once more we see that ionization is not caused by a high voltage, but by a high field strength.

Passive ionizers function equally well with positive and negative charges, but they suffer from the shortcoming that the corona discharge stops at a certain charge level, leaving a nonneutralized rest charge. Passive ionizers are therefore primarily used where the object is to remove large annoying charges, and where a minor rest charge is acceptable.

Sometimes passive ionizers are made as brushes of carbon fibers, which sweep over the charged material. Direct contact between the brush and the charged material does not improve the efficiency of the neutralization. The charges are not "wiped" off the material, but neutralized by oppositely charged air ions, and as a consequence the grounded brush should be kept at a (small) distance from the charged surface.

Electrical ionizers

In cases where a more or less complete neutralization of the charges is essential, ionization also at low charge levels is obtained by having the emitter points or

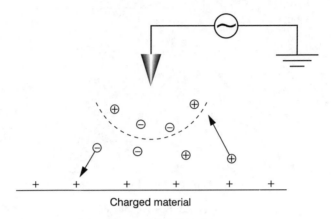

Charged material

Figure 5.4 AC ionizer

wires connected to a high voltage source, often an ordinary transformer ($\sim$ 5 kV). See Figure 5.4. Positive ions are emitted in that fraction of the positive half period where the emitter voltage exceeds the positive ionization voltage, and correspondingly for negative ions. Because of the lower negative ionization voltage, more negative than positive ions are produced, and unless the voltage supply is suitably biased, the operation of an AC ionizer may lead to a net (negative) charging of the material. It should also be kept in mind that ionization only takes place in a relatively short part of each period.

Uniform and balanced ion production can be achieved by the use of a double DC ionizer (see Figure 5.5), where alternate points are connected to adjustable positive and negative voltage sources. As suggested in the figure, the functioning of the "active" emitters may be supplemented by one or more passive ionizers.

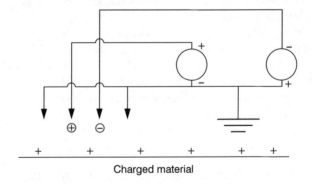

Charged material

Figure 5.5 Double DC ionizer

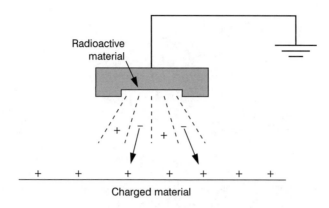

Figure 5.6 Radioactive ionizer

Radioactive ionizers

In a radioactive ionizer the radioactive source is placed upon a base material and covered with an extremely thin protective layer, often made of gold. The ionizer is mounted in such a way that the radiation is directed towards the space immediately in front of the charged material (see Figure 5.6). When one is dealing with relatively low levels of static charges and especially at places that are hard to get at, radioactive ionizers are very handy. They do not require electrical installation and they cannot cause potentially harmful electrical discharges. Their limitation lies in the fact that at high charge levels, one has to use impractically high (radio)activities, or the neutralization will take too long.

Usually radioactive ionizers utilize an alpha-active nuclide with a half-life of about half a year. Thus the active material is replaced at regular, not too long, intervals, and the device is not left unchecked for extended periods of time. As far as the radiological hazard is concerned, it is safe to assume that the direct *external* radiation from the ionizer is insignificant. If, however, the radioactive material, by accident or carelessness, is spread in the environment and, for instance, becomes airborne, it might be inhaled. The highly energetic alpha radiation may give an *internal* dose, which eventually may cause radiological damage to the respiratory tract, in the worst case initiating the growth of tumors. But with modern ionizers, the risk with proper handling and care is extremely low.

Ion blowers

The ionizers described above are all designed to be mounted in front (or back) of the charged material. In many cases, however, this approach is not practical or possible, and the ions have to be transported an appreciable distance from their site of production to the place of neutralization, usually aided by an air current.

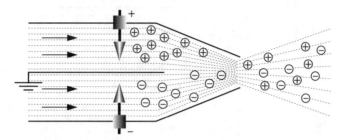

Figure 5.7 Ion blower

An ion blower, normally a benchtop device, is essentially an electrical (usually a single or double DC) or possibly radioactive ionizer encapsulated in a (at least partly) conductive house (often forming the counter electrode) with an air orifice or opening.

By blowing air past the region where ionization takes place, it is possible to create an air stream with a relatively high ion content (see Figure 5.7). Because of the small distance between emitter and counter electrode a substantial fraction of the ions formed will never reach the air outside the ionizer, and the ion concentration is further reduced because of diffusion, repulsion, and combination processes. For the type of bipolar ionizer shown, it is important that the air stream is balanced in terms of positive and negative ion concentrations, and most benchtop ionizers are therefore equipped with some kind of auto- or self-balancing feature.

Whole-room ionization

When working with very static-sensitive devices, the localized neutralization provided by normal ion blowers may not be sufficiently extensive. In such cases **whole-room ionization** may offer a good solution. The name is somewhat misleading, because the ionization with this kind of system does *not* take place in the room as a whole (as is the case with the ionization from airborne radioactivity), but in a rather limited volume, near the ceiling. Here a series of point emitters are mounted in a pattern, which may vary from system to system.

There are two essentially different principles for whole-room ionization systems. In one type of system alternate emitters are connected to positive and negative voltage supplies, and the ion production is continuous. In the other type all emitters are connected to the same voltage supply, delivering an AC voltage, which may be sinusoidal (50 or 60 Hz) or square-pulsed (1–2 Hz).

With the square-pulse technique ions are constantly produced (with alternate polarities), and because the pulses are fairly long, ions of a given polarity have a chance for moving away from the ionizer before ions of opposite polarity are produced and recombination sets in. This process can be enhanced by separating (shorter) positive and negative pulses by maybe half a second in the **stepped pulse** technique. The ions are brought down to work places and to items where neutralization is needed by field movement, diffusion, and often by a (laminary) air flow.

Unipolar ionizers

It has already been pointed out that in order to avoid recharging or overcompensation, proper neutralization of electrostatic charges by ionizing the air requires a balanced distribution of positive and negative ions around the charged object. It should thus be obvious that unipolar ionizers, emitting ions of one polarity only, are unsuited for neutralization purposes. If, however, the field from the emitters extends throughout the room where a unipolar ionizer is operated, airborne particulates will be removed from the air by the combined effect of the ions and the field. This feature will be discussed in Chapter 8, Applications of Static Electricity.

5. Ozone

With any kind of electrical discharges in atmospheric air, ozone (O_3) is produced. Ozone is probably best known as the part of the stratosphere that absorbs harmful UV radiation from the sun. Ozone is chemically extremely active. It has been used extensively, because of its effect on bacteria and germs, for disinfecting drinking water and in fruit storage and transport rooms, etc. The use of ozone-producing devices has even been suggested for improving the quality of indoor air.

However, ozone is also one of the most poisonous gases known. The maximum acceptable concentration is (in most countries) 0.1 ppm. Ozone will attack the respiratory tract when inhaled, and it appears that the effect may depend on the integrated exposure (like radioactive exposure), which makes the concept of a safe threshold limit value somewhat dubious.

Consequently, most modern instruments that utilize corona charging, like laser printers and photocopiers, are equipped with filters that adsorb most of the ozone produced. This, however, is not possible with systems intended to distribute ions to the surrounding air, as the ions would also be filtered out, probably even more effectively than the ozone. The ozone production rate increases with the corona current and, especially in constructions where a high emitter voltage is used together with short emitter-ground distances, the ozone levels should be monitored, especially in smaller rooms.

6. Liquids

The precautions previously described for abating static electricity can practically be utilized in connection only with solid materials. However, as already mentioned, many liquids are likely to be charged by flowing or spraying, and if the vapors of the liquids mixed with atmospheric air are explosive, it is obviously important to reduce the possibility of creating larger charge accumulations, normally by leading the charges away wherever possible.

To avoid the buildup of charges, first of all a suitable grounding of all conducting parts should be employed. If such a grounding is not possible, all conducting parts, e.g., filling tubes and containers, should be bonded. By suitable grounding high voltage differences between different parts of the structure cannot arise, but this kind of precaution does not reduce the charging of the liquid. It is, however, possible to moderate the flow pattern in such a way that the charge separation is kept to a minimum.

The charge separation rate is proportional to the linear flow velocity and to the tube diameter. At the same time, the decay resistance of the liquid is inversely proportional to the square of the tube diameter, and consequently the equilibrium voltage difference between the ends of the liquid column is proportional to the linear velocity and inversely proportional to the tube diameter. As an example, the following flow rates are known to give rise to very moderate charge separation: diethyl ether and carbon disulfide 1-2 $m \cdot s^{-1}$ (at small tube cross sections); esters, ketones and alcohols 9–10 $m \cdot s^{-1}$ (as a maximum).

When filling containers it is important to bring the filling tubes all the way to the bottom of the container in order to avoid free jets of liquids. At the start of a filling this requirement obviously cannot be fullfilled, and hence the flow rate should be kept low until the outlet is completely immersed in the liquid.

The charge of the liquid can sometimes be (partly) neutralized by means of a grounded metal screen immersed in the liquid. Such a precaution is of special importance when working with easily chargeable (and volatile) liquids like diethyl ether and carbon disulfide. The screen should be mounted so that it is not struck by jets of the liquid promoting turbulence and spraying.

Mixing of the liquid with other substances, especially colloids, may increase the charge separation rate. But, on the other hand, antistatic additives may often increase the conductivity of the liquid to such a degree that static charges can hardly be detected; these additives are used, for instance, when pumping gasoline at high flow rates.

Special Precautions

Railway tankers and stationary tank units normally do not need special grounding connections with the exception of the piping system for filling of containers. Road tankers and airplanes may, although it is not very likely, be charged during the drive or flight. Because of the possible serious consequences of a discharge in an explosive atmosphere, tankers and airplanes should be grounded before any transfer of fuel takes place. The connection of grounding or bonding wires should not be established close to the outlet of inflammable liquids or explosive vapor mixtures.

In pneumatic transport the use of atmospheric air or other gases containing oxygen should be avoided when handling volatile liquids. The transport gas should not pass through the system in order to avoid spraying.

Metallic pipe connections will normally be sufficiently conductive. But, as already mentioned, paint, rust, or grease can form insulating layers, making special wire connections across couplings necessary. When movable filling pipes (for instance, swinging links for filling of railroad tankers) are used, it is especially important to secure a safe grounding of the filling pipe, because during operation it will be very close to the grounded container at the outlet for the possibly charged liquid; thus a discharge might occur at the potentially most dangerous site.

All hoses should, if possible, be made of conductive rubber or of a material with a woven-in thread or net made of Monel metal or a similar material. It is also important to connect the thread and the couplings at the end of the hose securely. The resistance between the ends of the hose should be frequently checked and should not exceed a few megohms. Only couplings with conductive surfaces should be used, and connections should be carried out without the use of insulative grease or other fillers.

By handling relatively small volumes of liquids (less than, say 10 gallons), it is (except for especially volatile liquids like diethyl ether and carbon disulfide) sufficient to secure bonding of all conductive parts, especially metal funnels and containers. When handling liquids like diethyl ether it is advisable to use conductive containers with filling pipes brought down to the bottom of the recieving container, and any funnels must be properly grounded.

7. Powders, Dust, Aerosols

With dust/air mixtures and aerosols any charging occurs via interparticle friction, by friction between the particles and the surroundings (tubing or room walls), or by the production (for instance, spraying) process. For powders and dusts the following general rules apply:

- If the particle material is nonflammable, the charging itself does not pose any risk, as long as other inflammable materials are not present.
- When handling combustible materials it is important, when possible, to avoid fine partitioning because the ignition energy normally decreases with decreasing particle size. By adding an inert gas (like nitrogen) to the powder mixture, the ignition energy is increased and the explosion risk reduced.
- Inserting a grounded screen in the dust flow (and grounding any other conducting item in the system) may also reduce the charging.
- Flow rates should be kept to a minimum and elevated air humidity should be employed, when possible.

- Any interparticle friction will further charging processes, so any excess friction should be avoided. It is therefore better to transport powders on conveyer belts or in a free fall than to let the powders slide down a chute.

- Machinery and means of transportation should be made of conductive materials and grounded or at least placed on a conductive (and grounded) floor.

- If insulative materials have to be used, for instance in tubings, they should be metallized or made conductive in other ways, for instance, by the addition of carbon black.

- Finally, one should check frequently to see if the formation of films of dust, oil, etc., has ruined ways for charges to leak away.

Chapter 6

Static Electric Measurements

Most static electric measurements involve the determination of fundamental electric quantities like voltage difference, current, resistance, and capacitance. In practice, however, electrostatic measurements differ from traditional electrical measurements, first of all because the voltage differences are caused by static charge distributions, which are unable to deliver a current without ruining the voltages.

As a consequence, normal voltmeters, analog as well as digital, are unsuited for static measurements, because their functioning is based on a current, however small, passing through the instrument. Similarly, the resistances of interest in static electric context are often so high that they cannot be measured by traditional resistance measurement equipment. Further, investigations of electrostatic phenomena often require the measurement of specially static-related quantities like electric charge and electric field strength. Although the methods used for such measurements are primarily based on the principles for measuring voltage and current, a series of special requirements has to be considered.

1. Static Voltage

As already mentioned, to measure static voltages, it is necessary to use instruments that require no or at least only a very small passage of current. Such instruments are known as **electrometers** or **static voltmeters**. Ordinary voltmeters are primarily characterized by their internal resistance, or meter resistance. The higher the meter resistance is relative to the total resistance between the points to which the voltmeter is connected, the smaller is the influence of the voltmeter on the voltage to be measured. The concept of capacitance of an ordinary voltmeter is rarely of importance. The input resistance of electrometers should in principle be infinitely large, which in practice normally means higher than maybe $10^{14} \ \Omega$.

An electrometer can be considered as a capacitor, and the internal capacitance, the meter capacitance, plays a similar, although inverted, role to that of the meter resistance of an ordinary voltmeter. Suppose an insulated conductor with capacitance C is charged with a charge q. The conductor then has (from equation 2.16) a voltage

$$V = \frac{q}{C}$$

If we want to measure this voltage, we connect the conductor to an electrometer with meter capacitance C_i. The charge q will now distribute itself on the two capacitances, and the voltage measured, i.e., the reading of the electrometer, V_e, is

$$V_e = \frac{C}{C + C_i} V \tag{6.1}$$

If, for instance, $C_i = 20$ pF and $C = 200$ pF, we have

$$V_e = 0.91 \cdot V$$

The measured voltage of the charged conductor is thus 9% lower than it would have been (for the same total charge) if the conductor had not been connected to the electrometer. It appears that the smaller the meter capacitance, the smaller is the influence of connecting the electrometer on the voltage to be measured.

Electrometers may be divided into two groups: (1) **mechanical electrometers**, based on the force between charges causing the movement of a light movable system, and (2) **electronic electrometers**, in which a weak static effect is being electronically amplified. These are discussed in the following sections.

Mechanical Electrometers

Probably the oldest type of electrometer still in use is the **Braun electrometer** (see Figure 6.1), based on the same principle as the **electroscope**, constructed as early as 1785 by Bennet.

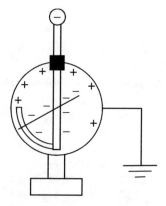

Figure 6.1 Braun electrometer

The Braun electrometer consists of a metal rod carrying an indicator and a ruled scale. The rod is insulately mounted inside a metal house with glass sides. The principle of the electrometer is as follows. Let the house be grounded and the insulated system connected to a, say negatively charged (insulated), conductor. The electrons on the conductor will distribute themselves on the conductor and the insulated system of the electrometer. By induction, a positive charge will be bound on the house, and the indicator will make a deflection caused by the attraction between its own charge and the charge on the house. The reading on the electrometer scale will give the common voltage of the electrometer and the charged conductor.

The range of voltages that a Braun electrometer can measure is approximately 100–5000 V. The isolated system of a Braun electrometer normally has a capacitance relative to the house on the order of 10–20 pF. Although this electrometer admittedly is rather old-fashioned and crude, it is easy to operate. Also, because of its low capacitance and consequent low interference with the voltage to be measured, it often presents a practical possibility of measuring medium to high static voltages.

Another type of mechanical electrometer is the **quadrant electrometer**, which looks more or less like an ordinary moving-coil instrument. Quadrant electrometers have capacitances and sensitivities in the same range as that of Braun electrometers.

About 50 to 100 years ago, a whole series of different mechanical electrometers were in common use, usually in scientific investigations. Some of these electrometers were extremely sensitive (down to about 1 mV), but they were difficult or at least cumbersome to handle and are today completely out of use. Mechanical electrometers can therefore be characterized as instruments of low capacitance and sensitivity and they suffer from the drawback that the reading cannot be (easily) automatically recorded.

Electronic Electrometers

In order to measure a static voltage of less than 100 V, and especially to record the voltage as a function of time, an electronic electrometer has to be used. Of the various types we shall briefly describe two, which work on different principles.

Vibrating electrometer

The principle of a **vibrating electrometer** (also called vibrating reed or capacitor electrometer) is as follows. Let the distance between the plates in a capacitor C vary with time, for instance, sinusoidally (see Figure 6.2). The capacitance of the capacitor will then vary correspondingly (equation 2.19).

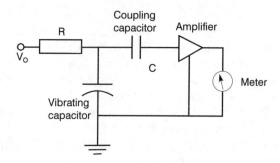

Figure 6.2 Vibrating electrometer

Let one plate of the capacitor be grounded and the other plate connected (through a high-ohmic resistor R) to a charged conductor with the voltage V_0. If the time constant RC is large compared to the period of the capacitor oscillations, an alternating voltage with an amplitude proportional to V_0 will be found across the capacitor C. This voltage can be amplified and measured, and V_0 has thus been determined without any current been drawn from the charged conductor.

The input resistance of a vibrating electrometer is essentially the leakage resistance of the vibrating and the coupling capacitor, and may thus be extremely and sufficiently high for most purposes. The meter capacitance is about 20–30 pF, but may, by the use of special couplings, be reduced to an effective value of 1–2 pF. The maximum voltage to be measured directly by a vibrating electrometer is normally 100 V or less. The sensitivity may be as high as a few μV. Vibrating electrometers are usually line operated.

Solid-state electrometer

Most modern electrometers are of the solid-state type, employing a MOSFET input, coupled to have the necessary $> 10^{14}$–10^{15} Ω input resistance. When the voltage to be measured is applied to the gate, the current through the transistor will be proportional to the voltage applied, and this current can be amplified and recorded in the normal way. The direct meter capacitance is normally a few tens of pF, but most electrometers are supplied with a series of capacitors, for instance from 100 pF to 0.1 μF, which can be connected between the input and ground. One application of this feature is discussed in Section 2.

Solid-state electrometers may be battery or line operated. Usually the voltage range covered is lower for the battery type (maybe 0–10 V) than for the line operated type (0–100 V). The sensitivity may be about 10–50 μV. Modern electrometers have a fairly low voltage range, normally not higher than about 100 V.

However, it is often necessary in static electric contexts to measure voltages on the order of kV. This apparent incompatibility can be overcome in two ways: by *capacitive voltage dividing* or by *field/voltage measurement*. These are discussed in Sections 2 and 3, respectively.

2. Capacitive Voltage Dividing

Normally the measurement range of a voltmeter is expanded simply by attaching a resistor R_e in series with the input of resistance R_i. If $R_e = (n - 1) \cdot R_i$, the range has been expanded by a factor of n. Because of the very high, and normally rather uncertain, input resistance of electrometers it is not possible to expand the measurement range of static voltmeters in the same way. The solution is to use this fact that the input resistance is so high that it, for practical purposes, can be considered infinite.

A capacitor C_e is attached in series with the input of the electrometer with meter capacitance C_m (see Figure 6.3). If the free end of C_e is connected to a conductor of voltage V, the relation between V and the electrometer reading V_m will be given by

$$V = \frac{C_m + C_e}{C_e} V_m \qquad (6.2)$$

If thus $C_m = (n - 1) C_e$, the range of the electrometer has been expanded by a factor n. Thus, by using the built-in capacitors and a fixed external capacitor, it is possible to change the range of the electrometer over several decades.

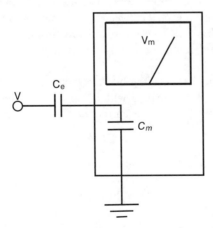

Figure 6.3 Capacitive voltage divider

EXAMPLE 6.1:

Let an electrometer have a full-scale reading $V_m = 1$ V and let C_m be chosen as 0.1 μF (10^{-7} F). If $C_e = 50$ pF ($5 \cdot 10^{-11}$ F), we can now measure voltages up to

$$V_{max} = \frac{10^{-7} + 5 \cdot 10^{-11}}{5 \cdot 10^{-11}} \cdot 1 \simeq 2000 \text{ V}$$

It should be noted that the capacitor C_e must have a high leakage resistance and be able to stand a voltage difference of

$$\frac{C_m}{C_e} V_m$$

which in the preceding example is 2000 V.

3. Field/Voltage Measurements

The method of determining high voltages by measuring a field strength will be described after a discussion of field measurements.

Currents

The currents of interest in connection with static electric phenomena may be currents from a charging process increasing the voltage of an insulated conductor or the field from an insulator, or decay currents reducing or limiting the voltages and fields. In both cases the currents are often very small, say 10^{-10} A or less. Most modern electrometers are supplied with a series of high-ohmic resistors (up to 10^{12} Ω), which can be connected between the electrometer input and ground, and by measuring the voltage difference across the resistor the current led to the electrometer can thus be determined. In this way it is possible to measure currents down to about 10^{-17} A.

Often, however, neither charging nor decay currents can be conveniently fed into an electrometer. When dealing with a capacitive system, i.e., an insulated conductor, with a capacitance C, the current to the system can be found from

$$q = CV$$

By differentiation, we have

$$I = \frac{dq}{dt} = C \frac{dV}{dt} \tag{6.3}$$

I is the difference between the charging and the decay current, so by measuring the rate of change of the voltage, it is possible to determine the net current to the system.

Resistance

Such resistances that are of interest in static electric contexts fall into two groups. In the first group we have the grounding resistances of conductors being either directly grounded or grounded through well-defined resistances of a few $M\Omega$ or less. Such resistances are easily measured by ordinary resistance measurement equipment. In the other group we have the grounding resistances of insulated conductors and the surface and bulk resistivities of insulators, involving the measurement of resistances from, say 10^8 Ω and up. Such resistances may be measured by special instruments like the **teraohmmeter**, or by the use of electronic electrometers.

Teraohmmeter

The principle of a teraohmmeter is shown in Figure 6.4. A voltage source A, for instance a battery-operated vibrator, delivers an output voltage, which can be adjusted to a fixed value V_N to be read on the static voltmeter E, when the switch is in position N. The resistance R_X to be measured is connected to the terminals B and C. Let the reading of the voltmeter with the switch in position X be V_X. The resistance R_X is then given by

$$R_X = R_N \frac{V_X}{V_N - V_X} \tag{6.4}$$

or

$$R_X = R_N \frac{1}{V_N/V_X - 1} \tag{6.5}$$

If V_N corresponds to a full reading of the voltmeter, it appears from equation (6.5) that, for a fixed value of R_N, the value of R_X corresponds to the reading V_X. The voltmeter scale can thus be directly divided into resistance values. Often a series of resistors (R_N) are builtin, making it possible to measure resistances up to about 10^{12} Ω, or one teraohm (TΩ).

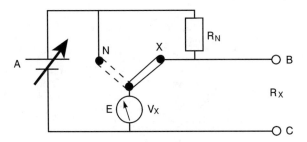

Figure 6.4 Teraohmmeter

For an insulated conductor the grounding (or decay) resistance may be determined by charging the insulated system and measuring the rate of decay (see Chapter 2, Section 16). Suppose the capacitance C of the system is known or can be estimated. If the system is charged to an initial voltage V_0, the voltage V of the system will decay with time t according to

$$V = V_0 \exp\left(-\frac{t}{\tau}\right) \tag{6.6}$$

where

$$\tau = RC \tag{6.7}$$

The grounding (decay) resistance of the system can thus be determined from

$$R = \frac{t}{C \ln \dfrac{V_0}{V}} \tag{6.8}$$

Resistivity

For insulating materials the total (integral) resistance is of little interest. The static electric behavior of insulating materials, however, is (partly) determined by their bulk and surface resistivities.

Bulk resistivity

The bulk resistivity of a sheet or plate material may be measured by an arrangement as shown in Figure 6.5. This corresponds in principle to the German norm DIN 53482 for the determination of resistivity of insulating materials.

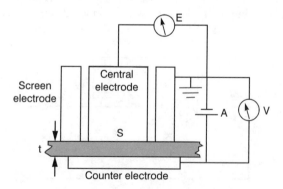

Figure 6.5 Measurement of bulk resistivity

The sample (of thickness t) to be tested is placed on a metal counter electrode. On top of the material is placed a cylindrical central electrode surrounded by a concentric cylindrical screen electrode. The screen electrode is grounded, and the central electrode is connected to a sensitive ammeter, E (normally an electrometer in current mode), the other side of which is grounded. The counter electrode is connected to one terminal of a voltage supply A, and the other terminal is grounded. The output voltage of the voltage supply is measured by the voltmeter, V.

Let the current measured on E be I and the voltage difference be V. The bulk resistance R is then, from equation (2.45),

$$R = \frac{V}{I} \qquad (6.9)$$

If the distance between the central and the screen electrode is much smaller than the radius of the central electrode, this is with good approximation the resistance of a cylindrical sample with a cross section equal to the area S of the central electrode and with a length equal to the thickness t of the sample. According to equation (2.46), the bulk resistivity, ρ, is given by

$$\rho = R\frac{S}{t} \qquad (6.10)$$

It is recommended to use a central electrode with a mass of about 1 kg (or rather a weight of 10 N) and a diameter of about 50 mm. The difference in radii for the two cylindrical electrodes should be about 1 mm. When measuring intermediate resistances, say, about 1 MΩ, contact resistances between the electrodes and the material may play a significant role. If the actual intrinsic resistivity of the material is wanted, it is therefore necessary to secure good contact, for instance, by means of conducting paste or wet filter paper. It should be stressed, however, that the value of the resistivity obtained under such conditions may be considerably lower than the effective resistivity of the material in a normal environment. The unit for bulk resistivity is Ωm.

Surface resistivity

To review the concept of surface resistivity and its determination, refer to the discussion in Chapter 2, Section 14.

The surface resistivity ρ_s, defined by equation (2.48),

$$\rho_s = \frac{E_s}{j_s} \qquad (6.11)$$

may be determined by an arrangement as shown in Figure 6.6. On top of the sample to be tested are placed two electrodes, both of length a and parallel to each other at a distance b. One of the electrodes is connected to one of the terminals of

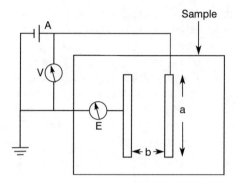

Figure 6.6 Surface resistivity, linear electrodes

a voltage supply, A, the other terminal of which is grounded. The output voltage of the voltage supply is measured by the voltmeter, V. The other electrode is connected to ground through a sensitive ammeter, E. If the output voltage is V_s and the current is I_s, the surface resistance R_s is

$$R_s = \frac{V_s}{I_s} \tag{6.12}$$

According to equation (2.51), the surface resistivity ρ_s is then given by

$$\rho_s = R_s \frac{a}{b}$$

When deriving equation (2.51), the field strength E_s between the electrodes was approximated with a voltage difference V_s over the electrode spacing b, and current density j_s with the total current I_s over the electrode length a, in both cases neglecting the stray fields at the end of the electrodes. It is possible (at least for extensive samples) to correct for these approximations, but a more direct way around the problem is to avoid the approximations by using cylindrical electrodes, as shown in Figure 6.7.

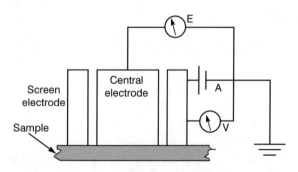

Figure 6.7 Surface resistivity, cylindrical electrodes

The setup is similar to the one shown in Figure 6.5 for the measurement of bulk resistivity. The central electrode is placed on top of the sample to be tested and connected to ground through the ammeter E. The screen electrode is connected to one terminal of the voltage supply A, the other terminal of which is grounded. The output voltage V_s of the voltage supply is measured on the voltmeter V. If the surface current between the screen and the central electrode is I_s, the surface resistance R_s is

$$R_s = \frac{V_s}{I_s}$$

If the radius of the central electrode is a, and the inner radius of the screen electrode is b, the surface resistivity ρ_s of the material is, according to equation (2.54),

$$\rho_s = R_s \frac{2\pi}{\ln\frac{b}{a}}$$

It appears from equation (2.51) as well as equation (2.54) that the unit for surface resistivity is Ω.

Effect of Electrode Geometry

There is no doubt that the quantity R_s, determined by equation (6.12), does represent the resistance between the electrodes used, either linear or cylindrical, for the sample chosen for the measurements. But it is not obvious that the calculated (differential) quantity ρ_s, determined from equation (2.51) or (2.54), actually represents a *material property*, characteristic for the material tested and independent of electrode geometry and dimensions (and sample shape and size).

In Figure 6.8 are shown some results of determining the surface resistivity of a sample consisting of a stack of 20 sheets of paper placed on, but insulated from, a grounded plane.

The resistivity was measured by two sets of linear electrodes (lengths 5 and 15 cm) and a set of cylindrical electrodes (central electrode radius $a = 25$ mm, and inner radius of screen electrode $b = 30, 35, 40, 65, 80,$ and 135 mm). The output voltage V_s was chosen as 200 V. For the cylindrical electrodes, the difference between the inner radius of the screen electrode and the radius of the central electrode was used as the electrode spacing.

It appears that for all three sets of electrodes the surface resistivity decreases rapidly with increasing electrode spacing up to about 3–4 cm. For larger distances, the surface resistivity measured by cylindrical electrodes [see equation (2.54)] seems fairly constant, whereas the quantity determined by the use of linear electrodes [see equation (2.51)], seems to show a steady, but slow, decrease with increasing electrode spacing. This is probably caused by the uncorrected effect of the stray field at the edges of the electrodes. There is no explanation of the small

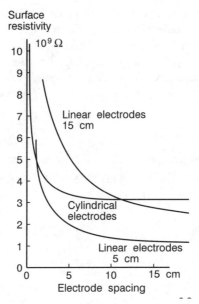

Figure 6.8 Variation of surface resistivity with electrode spacing and shape

difference in the results with the two sets of linear electrodes. But it should be pointed out that with the kind of uncertainty of definition of the quantities involved, all three sets of measurements must be considered to have yielded identical results, suggesting that the most important requirement when measuring surface resistivity is to avoid too small an electrode spacing.

Charge

Faraday pail

The classic, basic method of measuring a static charge is to place the charge on a capacitive system connected to an electrometer. If the collective capacitance of the system plus electrometer is C and the voltage, the reading of the electrometer, is V, the charge q is, according to equation (2.16),

$$q = CV$$

If the charge is located on an object of small dimensions, the charge may be measured by placing the object in an uncharged, insulated, conductive container connected to an electrometer (see Figure 6.9). Such a container is known as a **Faraday pail**.

If the charged object is conductive, the charge q will immediately be located on the outside of the capacitive system and will charge it to a voltage V to be read on the electrometer. The charge can thus be calculated from equation (2.16).

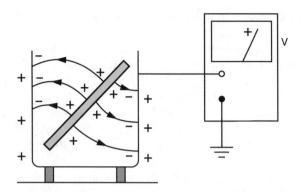

Figure 6.9 Charge measurement by use of Faraday pail

But even if the charged object is insulative the same method can be used. Let the charge q to be measured be positive. The field from q will by induction bind a negative charge on the inside of the pail, and even by the use of a fairly open pail this induced charge is very close to $-q$. The pail and electrometer as a whole were originally uncharged, so a charge $+q$ will be free to charge the system to a voltage V, and the charge q can again be calculated from equation (2.16). Even if the field from the charge causes a discharge and partial neutralization, the voltage V read on the electrometer will, with equation (2.16), give the total charge on the object immersed in the pail.

Corona transfer of charge

Another way of (apparently) transferring a charge to a capacitive system is through a corona discharge. Suppose the charge is placed on an extensive sheet of material that cannot conveniently be placed in a Faraday pail.

If an electrode, in the shape of a needle or thin wire, connected to an electrometer, is placed in front of the charged material (see Figure 6.10), at the electrode

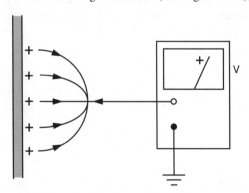

Figure 6.10 "Transfer" of charge through corona discharge

the field from the charge may exceed the breakdown field strength, causing positive and negative ions to be formed.

In this example negative ions will be attracted to the charged material, neutralizing the positive charge, and an equal number of positive ions will go to the electrometer and charge it to a voltage V, which again, by equation (2.16), will give the magnitude of the charge q being neutralized on the originally charged material. The process will stop when the field in front of the electrode no longer exceeds the breakdown field strength. Experience shows that if the surface of the material is carefully scanned by the electrode, about 80–90% of the total charge may have been neutralized.

It should be emphasized that the transfer of charge from the material is only apparent, and that the whole process consists of a sharing of an equal number of positive and negative ions formed in the air in front of the electrode.

Charge Density

In many cases the total charge on an object is of less interest than the distribution of charge, i.e., the charge density or charge per unit area, especially in the case of charged insulators. This quantity is normally deduced from measurement of the field strength in front of the charged object. We shall return to this subject when discussing field measurements.

Field Strength

The electric field strength is probably the single most important static electric quantity, but it is also the most difficult one to measure and interpret. All measurements of electric fields are based on the ability of a field to cause induction in a conductor (see Chapter 2, Section 4).

Let an insulated conductor A be placed in the field from a positively charged body B (see Figure 6.11). The field will bind an induced charge $-q$ on A. From equation (2.10) it follows that

$$|q| = S\varepsilon_0 E \tag{6.13}$$

where S is the area of the conductor facing the field and E is the field in front of the conductor. The field E is thus given by

$$E = \frac{|q|}{S\varepsilon_0} \tag{6.14}$$

The charge q can be determined in two different ways: by the *probe method* and by a *field mill* (or *rotating field meter*).

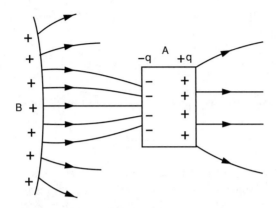

Figure 6.11 Field measurement by induction

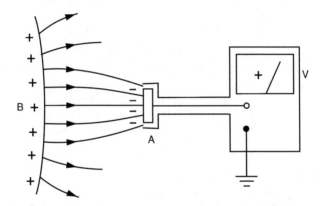

Figure 6.12 Field measurement by the probe method

Probe method

Let the conductor A from Figure 6.11 be a shielded disk connected to an electrometer with a (total) input capacitance C (see Figure 6.12). The free charge $+q$ on A will then charge the electrometer to a voltage V, given by equation (2.16). From equations (6.14) and (2.16) we then get

$$E = \frac{C}{S\varepsilon_0} V \qquad (6.15)$$

The reading V of the electrometer will thus give the field strength E in front of the probe.

This method, however, has an intrinsic possibility of error. If the probe is directly charged (for instance by airborne charged particulates) by an excess charge Δq, this will cause an excess reading ΔV on the electrometer, and the field will be over- or underestimated by an amount of

$$\Delta E = \frac{\Delta q}{S\varepsilon_0} = \frac{C}{S\varepsilon_0}\Delta V \qquad (6.16)$$

This possibility of error may, however, be avoided by the use of a *field mill* or *rotating field meter*.

Field mill

In a field mill, the conductor A from Figure 6.11 is segmented (see Figure 6.13) and connected to ground through a resistor R. In front of A is placed a grounded, similarly segmented, electrode B, which is rotated. If the system is placed in an electric field E, the electrode A will alternatively be screened from and exposed to the field. In the latter situation, a charge q is bound on the electrode given by

$$|q| = S\varepsilon_0 E$$

where S again is the area of the electrode. An equivalent, equally large, opposite charge will flow through R to ground. In the screened situation, the field-bound charge is released and will thus flow to ground, and so on. The result is that across R an alternating voltage is created, the amplitude of which is proportional to the field strength E at the surface of the electrode. This voltage can be easily amplified and measured, and by the use of of a phase-sensitive amplifier the polarity (direction) of the field can also be determined.

Field distortion

It should be stressed that the field strengths measured by either the probe or the field mill method refer to the field at the surface of the probe or electrode, and, as

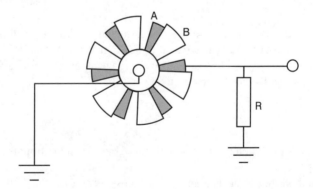

Figure 6.13 Field measurement by a field mill

suggested in Figures 6.11 and 6.12, this field may be significantly different from (larger than) the field at the surface of the charged object.

The placing of the field meter in the field is said to distort the field to be measured. This source of error can be (partly) avoided by surrounding the field probe by a grounded (normally plane) screen (see Figure 6.14). The field lines will distribute themselves more or less evenly on the screen and the probe, and the field measured, which is still the field at the site of the field meter, will be approximately the same as the field in front of the charged object. It should, however, be emphasized that if the charged object is a conductor, the charge located on the surface facing the field meter increases strongly with decreasing distance to the field meter.

Charge density from field strength

As mentioned earlier, the charge density may be deduced by measuring the field strength in front of the charged surface. From equation (2.10) the charge density σ *on the field probe* is given by

$$\sigma = \varepsilon_0 E \tag{6.17}$$

where E is the field strength measured. This procedure gives a reasonable estimate of the charge density (on a conductor) in situations resembling the conditions in Figure 6.14.

For a charged insulator the situation is more complicated because the field from a charge on a given part of the surface may extend through the insulator and into the surrounding air to grounded objects on the other side.

In Figure 6.15 is shown a charged, thin insulating plate A. Behind A at a distance x is placed a grounded plate B parallel with A. In front of A at a distance y is placed a field meter surrounded by a grounded plate C also parallel to A. If the

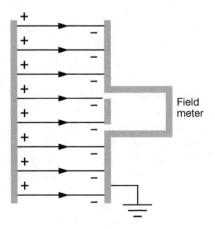

Field meter

Figure 6.14 Alignment of electric field

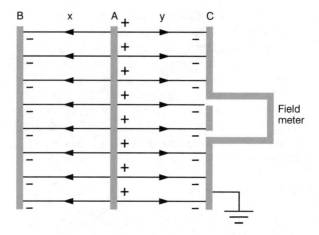

Figure 6.15 Field from charged insulator

field strength measured is E, the surface density σ calculated from equation (6.17) is related to the true charge density σ_t on the insulating surface by

$$\sigma = \sigma_t \frac{x}{x + y} \qquad (6.18)$$

If the charged insulating surface thus is placed close to grounded items, the surface charge density may be grossly underestimated. If the finite thickness of the insulator is taken into consideration, the calculations are somewhat more complicated, but the general picture is the same.

Field/Voltage Measurements

The basic relation between field strength and voltage difference

$$V_A - V_B = \int_A^B \boldsymbol{E} \cdot d\boldsymbol{a}$$

may also be used for the measurement of static voltages.

In Figure 6.16 is shown a field meter on which is mounted a metal cylinder B. In B is placed an insulated disk C parallel to the sensing electrode A of the field meter. The distance between A and C is d. If a positively charged insulated conductor A is connected to C, an electric field E is established between A and C.

If this field were homogeneous, the voltage V of the conductor A would be given by

$$V = Ed \qquad (6.19)$$

where E is the reading of the field meter. This, however, is not the case, but the field strength E measured on the field meter will still be proportional to the volt-

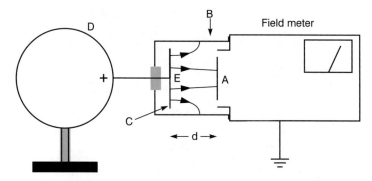

Figure 6.16 Measurement of voltage by a field meter

age *V*. It is thus a simple procedure experimentally to calibrate the field meter for voltage measurements—but of course only in connection with charged insulated conductors.

Hand-held meters

A popular way of spotting electrostatic charges is by the use of the various types of hand-held meters, sometimes known as **static locators**. These instruments may be of the probe or the field mill type. They are very covenient to use, as long as their shortcomings are remembered and taken into consideration.

First of all, they should always be grounded when used. If the instrument is not directly grounded and the operator is standing on an insulating floor covering, a charge on (and consequently a voltage of) the operator may render any reading of the instrument meaningless. Often though, it is sufficient that the operator grounds herself and ensures that she does not become charged during the measurements.

If the instrument is calibrated as a field meter, i.e., the scale is in V/m (or kV/m), the reading will give the field strength *at the sensing element*, providing the calibration has been carried out in a homogeneous field, for instance by an arrangement as shown in Figure 6.14. Some instruments are graded in V (or kV) and state a certain distance from the charged object at which the measurement should be performed. If this instruction is followed, the reading *may* give the voltage of the charged object, *but only if the object is a conductor with the same dimensions as the one used for the calibration*. And this is hardly ever the case.

When used with charged insulators, which is probably the most common use, the concept of a voltage (surface potential) is at best a very dubious one (see Chapter 2, Section 7) and it cannot be determined in such a simple way. Hand-held meters, when properly used, are excellent for a *qualitative* assessment of static charges and their polarities. But pointing a hand-held meter (or for that matter a regular field meter) towards a charged insulator, say a plastic box, and pronouncing that the box has a voltage of 2000 V, is unprofessional.

Chapter 7

Static Electricity and People

As suggested in the introduction, static electricity has often (at least in some parts of the world) in a rather unspecific way been attributed effects on human beings—usually unhealthy and/or unpleasant effects. In this chapter we shall discuss such effects that are documented or at least have a scientifically based possibility of being real. •

1. Charging of Persons

Charging by Walking

The most common way in which a person can become electrostatically charged is by walking across an insulating floor covering. We have already discussed the physics of this problem in detail (see Chapter 4, Section 7). In the example shown in Figure 4.6, the maximum (equilibrium) voltage of the person charged was about 3 kV, but under special conditions, especially very low relative humidity, voltages as high as 10–15 kV may be encountered. The often quoted upper value of 35 kV (see for instance Owen McAteer's *Electrostatic Discharge Control*, p. 356) is (even at very low humidity) in this author's belief apocryphal. Long before this value is reached, even if the charging conditions were theoretically right, corona or other types of discharges would start from the person's ears, nose, or fingertips, keeping the voltage down.

Charging From Clothing

It has often been claimed that wearing certain types of clothing, such as nylon fabrics, can charge a person electrostatically. This, however, can only happen under two conditions: (1) The clothing is rubbed against other surfaces in the surroundings, for instance, a chair seat. If a person wearing insulating outer wear gets up from a chair, her voltage may be as high as that from walking on an insulating carpet. (2) The insulating piece of clothing is completely removed from the body. The effect of this kind of charging is what you experience when you take off a sweater or blouse and hear a crackling or feel a discharge to your ear. What you hear or feel is not the charging, but on the contrary, the discharging of the charges being separated by removing the piece of clothing. This also explains why the very wearing of the insulating clothing does not cause a charging of the person. Although the various layers of clothing may rub against each other or against the skin and cause a charge separation, the charge on the person caused by the clothing will essentially be the sum of equally large opposite charges and thus not contribute to the total voltage of the person.

Other Modes of Charging

People may, however, also be charged in other ways, primarily by contact with already charged materials. A well-known example of this is the handling of photocopies. When the copies leave the machine, they will often be heavily charged, in spite of the use of passive and other ionizers. Even if the copies fall in a grounded metal tray, they lose very little of their charge. A person picking up a bunch of such copies may cause a discharge to or from the copies, causing a part of the charge to be neutralized, and an equally large charge goes to the person (see also Figure 6.10). The rest charge will induce charges on the person. If she is standing on an insulating floor, she will be charged to a voltage caused by a charge almost equal to the total charge on the copies.

There are many other examples of this kind of, direct or inductive, charging, such as the pouring of insulating powders or liquids from hand-held containers, or just standing near a charged sheet of plastic. If the person performing these actions is not properly grounded, this may result in a considerable body voltage.

2. Effects of Charges on Persons

An insulated, charged person may, like any other insulated, charged conductor, produce a discharge, for instance a spark, through the surrounding air or cause a current pulse through some suitably conducting grounding path. These phenomena have already been discussed in Chapter 4. In this chapter we will concern ourselves with the effect of the charging on the person herself.

Electric shocks

The best-known and most direct effect of an electric charge on a person is the shock a charged person may receive by discharging to a grounded, or at least uncharged, conductor or to another person.

A person may walk around a floor charged to a voltage of, say 5 kV, without any discharge taking place because the breakdown field strength (3 MV/m) is not exceeded at any point. If she now reaches for a door handle the field around her hand (or maybe around her fingertips) will be distorted (see Figure 4.4), the breakdown field may be exceeded, a discharge may occur, and the person may feel an electric shock. The level of body voltage at which these shocks become noticable or even unpleasant has often been discussed and it is fair to say that this is a very individual and uncertain matter.

At levels of 700 V or lower no sparks can occur at all. At such low voltages the breakdown distance is too low to allow the ionization to develop to a spark. There are very few investigations on the question of (non)acceptable body voltages, primarily because test persons probably react differently if they know they are going to experience an electric shock than if they get the shock unexpectedly. Such tests should therefore preferably be performed as an undisclosed part of completely different experiments.

It does seem, however, that hardly any people will feel discomfort at voltages around 1000–1500 V. At 2000 V many people start complaining, and above 3000 V almost everybody will characterize the shocks as unpleasant. There is also some indication that women seem to be more sensitive to electric shocks than men, i.e., women can detect discharges at lower voltages. (This, of course, does not necessarily mean that they also complain more than men!)

Indirect Effects

It has often been suggested that static electric charging of people might have effects other than the purely physical ones described above; effects that could rather be considered physiological or hygienic. Many people may feel discomfort in certain types of dwellings, experiencing headaches, tiredness, dry skin or mucosa, or feeling that the air is stuffy, etc. They may also experience static electric chargings in the form of electric shocks.

People often feel that the two types of phenomena are tied together, and the static charging is considered to be the cause of the lack of well-being. But there are no trustworthy scientific investigations suggesting any direct physiological or hygienic effects caused by static charging of a person. There is, however, one way in which static charging of a person may indirectly lead to a physiological effect, and that is through the electric field surrounding the charged person.

Electric Field and Airborne Particulates

It has been demonstrated that an operator exposed to the (positive) field from a computer monitor may experience a considerable increase in the plateout of airborne particulates on her face. The particles do not necessarily have to be (negatively) charged, although such particles obviously will be moved in the field. Particles that can be polarized (or are even conductive) will move along the field lines in the direction where the field increases, i.e., towards the face of the operator. And the same kind of effect can obviously happen if the person is charged, and thus surrounded by an electric field. The static charge may thus cause airborne particles, some of them harmless, some of them possibly less innocent, to deposit on exposed skin. It should be stressed that it has *not* been scientifically shown that this effect leads to increases in skin diseases. But the possibility does exist.

One more thing should be mentioned in this context. A person sitting in front of a computer may be exposed to a field of 20 kV/m or more for periods of several hours, but an electrostatically charged person will only be surrounded by a strong field as long as she is highly charged; also any time she receives an electric shock, she is instantly brought to zero voltage, and the field effect disappears. The high voltage and the strong field will normally exist only for relatively short periods.

Electric Fields and Ions

The field around a charged person will obviously also affect the ions in the air. If the person is negatively charged, more positive and fewer negative ions will plate out on her skin, but more interesting is the fact that the number of ions of both polarities *inhaled* will be lower than if the person is not charged. For a negatively charged person, negative ions will be repelled and positive ions will be attracted to the skin and thus moved out of the air flow to the nostrils or the mouth. Therefore, if the number of ions inhaled has any physiological or other significance, an electrostatic charge of the person may interfere with this.

Almost from their discovery around 1900 air ions have been attributed rather specific as well as more diffuse effects on people's well-being. Let us give an example of each of these types of effects. It was long claimed that an excess of negative ions in inhaled air would increase the frequency of the mucociliary function in the trachea and thus enhance the natural cleaning of the airways. An excess of positive ions has been said to have a corresponding detrimental effect. As an example of a more diffuse effect, it has often been claimed that air with an excess of negative ions is fresh, whereas positive ions make the air heavy and stuffy. Unfortunately, no alleged effects of ions in the inhaled air have ever been satisfactorily scientifically documented.

As far as the cilia effect is concerned, it was proven not to exist as far back as 1971, but oddly enough, the claim of effect still appears now and then. As far as the negative ions/fresh air claim is concerned, it should be kept in mind that the fresh air on a mountaintop is rich in positive ions, whereas the stuffy air beneath and during a thunderstorm has an excess of negative ions. Obviously there is more to air freshness and stuffiness than just ions.

But it is a fact that a charged person will inhale fewer ions of both polarities than an uncharged person, and as we have said, it has not yet been proven if this has any significance for a person's well-being. In the next chapter, Applications of Static Electricity, an example of the use of ions and an electric field for air cleaning will be discussed. The effect of this principle is sometimes misinterpreted as an effect of ions being inhaled.

Chapter 8

Applications of Static Electricity

In the previous chapters we have discussed the effects of mostly fortuitous static charge distributions, and most of the time we have considered static electricity and static electric fields as only causing inconveniences for mankind. But this attitude is not really fair. An increasing number of important processes, industrial and otherwise, are totally or in part based on electrostatic phenomena. Although the use of these processes is common and widespread, many people do not realize their static background. Among the many examples of such processes let us mention *precipitation of airborne particulates, separation of different materials, electrostatic surface treatment (with liquids as well as powders)*, and *electrostatic copying and printing*. Specific applications are constructions like *electrostatic generators, motors, speakers, and microphones*.

Many electrostatic processes involve the handling of very small and light particles, and the following features are common and characteristic for such processes:

(a) The force from an electric field on a small charged particle may be much larger than gravity.

(b) It is very easy to monitor the electric force by monitoring the applied field.

(c) The electric forces acting upon airborne particles interfere insignificantly with the air and its movement.

For practically all applications of static electricity one or more materials must be electrified. The electrification may take place in several ways. The more important ones are:

- Corona electrification
- Contact and triboelectrification
- Polarization or induction in an electric field.

Often two or more electrification processes are active. For some of the fields of application mentioned here, we have, for example:

119

- Precipitation: corona
- Separation: corona and triboelectrification
- Surface treatment (coating and flocking): contact and triboelectrification and induction
- Copying and printing (imaging): corona, triboelectrification, induction, and conduction.

1. Precipitation

Many industrial processes produce various kinds of airborne particulates to an extent that makes it necessary to clean the air before it is released. A prime example of this is the production of fly ash in coal-fired electric power generation, but steel and cement production, fertilizer processing, and many other chemically oriented processes also create particulate air pollutants on a large scale. Even everyday, household activities like cooking and cleaning, not to mention smoking, will produce particle concentrations in the air at often unacceptable levels.

Although particulates can be removed from the air by mechanical filters, it should be stressed that, especially as far as industrial pollution is concerned, the use of electrostatic prepicipitation is by far the most important remedial method. Electrostatic precipitation is also the oldest application of static electric principles to be put to industrial use, going back to Cottrell, who built his first precipitator in 1907.

Electrofilter

The basic principle of an electrostatic precipitator or electrofilter, whether it is used in a power plant or in the living room, is shown in Figure 8.1. A (series of) thin wire(s) is kept at a high potential with respect to ground, causing a corona

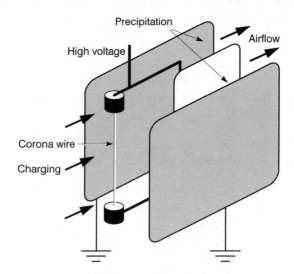

Figure 8.1 Electrofilter

discharge to take place in a thin sheath around the wire. If the wire is kept at a negative potential, the negative ions formed will move away from the wire to grounded surroundings. The air to be cleaned is drawn past the corona wires, and the ions will tend to attach to particles in the air. The charged particles are carried into a precipitation volume, where an electric field is established between a series of electrodes alternately grounded and kept at the same polarity as (but often at a lower potential than) the corona wires. The particles will be moved towards and deposited on the grounded electrodes from where they can later be removed by various means, depending on the type of filter.

In industrial plants, big mechanical shakers and scraping arrangements may be needed for cleaning; with househould devices it may be enough to place the filter unit in the dishwasher every other week.

An electrofilter may be operated at positive as well as negative voltages. For a given voltage, the corona current and thus the ionization are higher at negative voltages, but, as explained in Chapter 5, so is the ozone production. The efficiency of an electrofilter for removing particles larger than approximately 0.5 μm from the air may be close to 100%. But obviously the effect of an electrofilter on a given source of air pollution, like smoking, is also determined by the filtration rate, i.e., the volume of air passing through the filter per unit time and especially this rate taken relative to the volume of the room to be treated and the strength of the pollution source. The advantage of an electrofilter is obviously that the particulate material plated out is deposited inside the filter from where it can be fairly easily removed. A disadvantage is that the functioning of the filter requires the operation of a fan, which involves some power consumption and a certain amount of noise.

Open Field Ionizer

An open field ionizer is essentially a corona electrode, in the shape of a sharp metal needle or a bundle of thin carbon fibers, connected to a high voltage supply and placed unscreened in a room. (See Figure 8.2). The electrode, somewhat misleadingly called an *emitter* see (Chapter 5, Section 4), will be surrounded by an electric field extending to all grounded surroundings, including the faces of the room, furniture, and people.

If the potential of the emitter is high enough ($\approx$ 2–20 kV) ions of both polarities are formed in a small volume in front of the emitter, and the ions of the same polarity as the emitter will move away along the field lines. If the ions on their way meet airborne particles they may attach to them, thus charging the particles. These charged particles will now move (slowly) and eventually plate out on the surfaces where the field lines end. An open field ionizer thus operates on the same basic principles as an electrofilter. Both devices remove particulates from the air by (1) creating ions by a corona discharge, (2) charging the particulates, and (3) moving the charged particles out of the air by the action of an electric field.

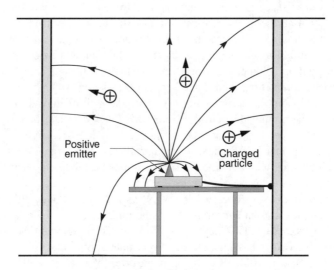

Figure 8.2 Open field ionizer

But whereas an electrofilter deposits the particles in a well-defined region from which they can be removed, the plateout of particles caused by an open field ionizer takes place in a more incidental way and often in a very uneven pattern. The plateout rate will be high at surfaces where the field strength is high, i.e., in the neighborhood of the ionizer, and the result is often an unattractive smudging of the surroundings of the ionizer. It is possible to reduce this effect by the use of a suitable counter electrode, called a **collector**. But although a collector reduces the smudging near the ionizer, the major part of the particles still plate out on the walls, ceiling, etc.

The advantages of an open field ionizer over an electrofilter are small size, low power consumption, and noiselessness. An open field ionizer works equally well with negative and positive voltages except in the case where the purpose is to remove the short-lived airborne daughter products of radon. For this purpose positive fields and ionization are by far the most effective.

It has sometimes been claimed that an open field ionizer is suited for neutralizing static electric charges. This is not the case. Because an open field ionizer produces ions of only one polarity there is even a risk that the operation may charge a material instead of neutralizing it.

2. Separation

The principle of electrostatic precipitation, as explained above, is a charging of airborne (solid or liquid) particles with the same polarity, which consequently makes them move in the same direction in an electric field. The principle of electrostatic separation, on the other hand, is to charge the components in particulate

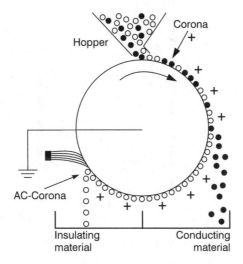

Figure 8.3 Electrostatic drum separator

mixtures with opposite polarities (or leave conducting components uncharged) and subsequently separate the components, by mutual repulsion or by an external electric field, and possibly aided by gravity.

Figure 8.3 shows a **drum separator**. A mixture of conducting and insulating particles is fed from a hopper onto the grounded drum. All the particles are charged by a corona discharge, positively in the case shown. When the particles leave the corona region, the conductive particles loose their charge to the drum and move away by gravity (and "centrifugal" forces). The insulating particles stick to the drum until they are removed by a brush or scraper, possibly assisted by an AC corona discharge.

Often the charging of particles to be separated is achieved by contact between the different particles or between the particles and an external material. The exchange of charge depends upon factors like the properties of the materials themselves, the state of their surfaces, and external parameters like electric fields and temperature gradients across interfaces. When the particles are separated, a part of the charges exchanged may remain on the respective surfaces, and the motion of the particles may be controlled by an electric field.

In Figure 8.4 is shown an example of the application of this principle in the electrostatic separation of iron ore from sand by the use of a fluidized bed. Under certain temperature and humidity conditions, iron ore in the form of Fe_2O_3 will charge positively because of triboelectric effects by contact with steel as well as sand. The mixture of iron ore and sand is fluidized over a perforated plate of stainless steel by means of an air jet. The steel plate is kept at a high potential, creating an upward electric field in the fluidization region. The positively charged Fe_2O_3

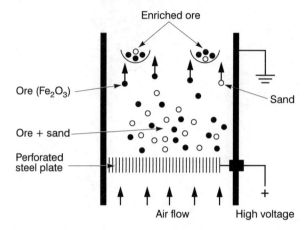

Figure 8.4 Iron ore/sand separator

particles will move upwards because of the field into the transport region, where they can be collected in various ways, for instance, on conveyer belts running over grounded rollers. The Fe_2O_3 particles, being somewhat conductive, will get an extra (field-induced) positive charge by contact with the positive steel plate, but the sand, principally consisting of insulating SiO_2 particles, may by contact with the steel charge positively as well as negatively, and primarily through triboelectric effects. As a result the ore collected has a much higher relative content of iron than the untreated ore, as the negatively charged sand particles are being retained.

If the polarity of the steel plate is changed to negative, the efficiency of separation is drastically reduced because the field-induced charging of the Fe_2O_3 particles is partly neutralized by the triboelectric charging.

Table 8.1 shows a few of the very large number of mixtures of materials in particle form that can be separated electrostatically with a commercial benefit.

Table 8.1 Electrostatically separable mixtures

Asbestos/silicates	Limestone/silicates
Coal/pyrite	Nickel/copper ore
Coal/shale	Zirconium/sand
Copper ore/silicates	Barley, rice, soybeans/
Coke/iron	rodent excrements
Diamond/silicates	Cocoa beans/shells
Feldspar/quartz	Cotton seeds/stems
Fly ash/carbon	Grain/garlic seeds
Iron/silicates	Nut meats/shells
Kaolin/iron contaminations	Photographic film/paper
	Polyvinyl/polyester

3. Coating

Almost all articles and products manufactured and used today have been coated in one or more ways. This is true for the paper we write on, the clothes we wear, the cars we drive, the furniture we sit in, etc. For practical, economic, and environmental reasons, it is desirable to use only the necessary amount of material, and this consideration makes electrostatic coating superior to most other methods.

An electrostatic coating process may take place in the following manner. The object to be coated is placed in such a way that its surface is freely accessible. The coating material is rendered airborne in the form of small particles, liquid or solid, in the region in front of the object. The particles are charged with one polarity and the object with the opposite (or the object is grounded). Electrostatic attraction between the opposite charges causes the particles to move towards the object and plate out on its surface.

There are a series of variations of this process, but here we shall discuss only a single example, where the coating material is in liquid form (see Figure 8.5). The objects to be coated are placed on a grounded conveyer system, which will bring them close to a system of corona electrodes connected to a suitable high voltage supply (for instance 100,000 V). The ions formed by the corona discharge will move in the field towards the grounded objects. A fine mist of the coating material is sent from one or more spray guns into the ionization region, where the droplets will catch ions from the air, become charged, and move onto the grounded objects.

It follows from this explanation that the objects to be coated have to be (somewhat) conductive. In many cases this can be achieved, even with normally insulating materials, by working at a temperature of a few hundred degrees centigrade. As suggested in Figure 8.5, the air is sucked past the moving objects with a velocity in the opposite direction. A charged particle will thus move because of the air flow as well as because of the electric field. Because the field lines end on all parts of the surface of the object, although very unevenly, such areas that are, so to

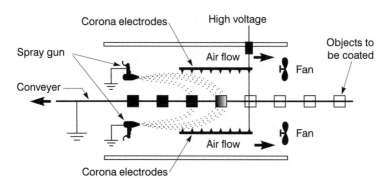

Figure 8.5 Electrostatic spray coating

speak, in the shade will also be coated. Often the objects to be coated are rotated during the passage of the field in order to make the coating more even.

The advantage of an electrostatic surface coating over, for instance, traditional spray painting lies partly in the ability of the field to reach and coat areas in the dark and partly in a very essential reduction in the necessary amount of coating material. It is characteristic, for the example shown, that the droplets are formed by spraying, charged by ion capture, brought into the electric field by an air flow, and deposited by a combined effect of the field and the air movement. The spraying will, however, cause a certain waste of coating material. In order to reduce this waste the particles may be formed at a relative low velocity in a strongly divergent field. In this way the particles may be charged from the start and move primarily by field forces towards the objects to be coated.

Figure 8.6 shows an example of an electrostatic spray device based on this principle. A disk is made to rotate around a vertical axis at, say a couple of thousands revolutions per minute. The coating material is fed to the center of the disk. Because of the rotation and the "centrifugal" force (or rather the lack of centripetal force), the material will spread across the disk and leave the rim as irregular drops. If the disk is given a high voltage with respect to the surroundings, the field at the rim will be strongly inhomogeneous; this will cause the drops to be charged by induction and to split up into small droplets, each carrying a large charge. The objects to be coated are kept at ground potential and brought into the field by a conveyer in a circle around the disk while rotating slowly. If there were no electric field, the coating would only apply in a narrow band on the objects, but because of the field the coating may spread out to a width on the order of half the distance between the disk and the objects.

There is no fundamental reason that the material to be deposited electrostatically has to be in liquid form, and there are actually many processes where the deposition of a powder on a surface is governed or enhanced by electric forces. The powder may be made airborne, e.g., by the use of a fluidized bed or by a disk system similar to the one shown in Figure 8.6.

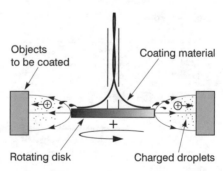

Figure 8.6 Electrostatic disk coating

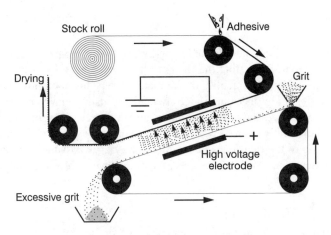

Figure 8.7 Manufacturing of sandpaper

Manufacture of Sandpaper

A surface coating of a completely different type from the ones described above is the manufacturing of sandpaper. Figure 8.7 shows the principle of this process.

With two plane electrodes, one grounded and the other connected to a high-voltage supply, an electric field is established. A continuous belt of a suitable (semiconducting) material passes through the field in contact with the lower electrode. The paper or textile to become the backing of the sandpaper is fed from a stock roll through the field in contact with the upper electrode. Before the paper enters the field, a layer of adhesive is placed on the side of the paper that will face downwards.

The abrasive, for instance, sand or ground agate, is fed from a hopper onto the lower belt outside the field. When the abrasive enters the field the grains will be polarized and also charged directly with the same polarity as the lower electrode. The grains may align their longest axis with the field, and when the field strength is high enough (about 1 MV $\cdot$ m^{-1}) they will move towards the upper electrode and embed themselves in the adhesive with a sharp tail sticking out. If a grain hits a point already occupied by another grain, the late arriver will be neutralized, charged with the opposite polarity, and repelled. It will then move back to the lower belt, where the process may start all over again. When the grit-covered face leaves the field, loose material is removed by means of a shaker, and the adhesive set in a drier. The electrostatic deposition of the abrasive will give a more uniform distribution and a more beneficial orientation of the single grains than is possible by a purely mechanical process.

Flocking

Flock is made by gluing bundles of aligned, short fibers, for instance nylon, onto a suitable material. By cutting the fibers to the same height a suede- or felt-like material is produced. The quality of the material depends upon how evenly and parallel the fibers are distributed and oriented. By using a principle very much like the one described above for sandpaper, a high degree of uniform distribution and parallel orientation can be achieved. By shaping the electrodes, and thereby the orientation of the field lines, in a suitable way, it is possible to produce patterns and lettering, as used, for instance, on sweaters and "brocade" wallpaper.

4. Imaging

The distribution of a static charge on an insulating surface can be extremely inhomogeneous, and over the years many attempts have been made to visualize this distribution. The best-known method was the application of fine powders like lycopodium or resin.

Conversely, a related process is to try to transfer the differences in printing or drawing density of an ordinary picture or drawing to differences in charge density on a suitable surface. If this electric picture can then be transferred back to a visible image on a sheet of paper or a screen, we have an electrostatic copy of the original picture. This can be done in several ways, but here we shall give only the main features of the electrophotographic process known as xerography.

Xerography is based on the physical phenomenon called **photoconductivity**, i.e., some materials have a much higher conductivity when they are exposed to light than when they are in the dark. This is true for a material like selenium (amorphous), but several chemical compounds, e.g., zinc oxide (specially treated), can also be used.

Let us consider a sheet of paper of a suitable high conductivity, covered by a layer of zinc oxide. The backside of the paper is placed in contact with a grounded conductor (see Figure 8.8a). By means of a corona wire at a positive direct voltage of, for instance, 5 kV the zinc oxide layer is charged with a positive charge, while kept in the dark. This charge binds by induction an equally large negative charge in the paper, and the resulting field in front of the layer is therefore very weak. As long as the zinc oxide is not exposed to light, the charges in the electric double layer will recombine very slowly.

A picture of the object to be copied is now formed briefly on the zinc oxide by a suitable optical system (Figure 8.8b). On the areas exposed to the light the charges will disappear (combine), partly or totally, and what is left is a charge distribution corresponding to the distribution in density of the optical picture. Apart from the brief exposure the zinc oxide is kept in the dark during the rest of the process.

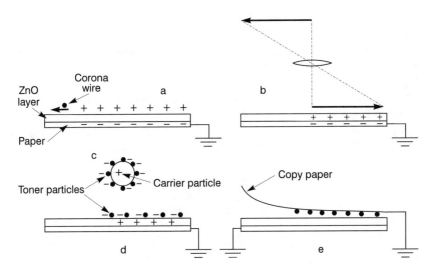

Figure 8.8 Xerographic photocopying

The "electric picture" is now brought into contact with a toner, which consists of small (about 1–10-μm) plastic particles to which is added carbon. The toner particles are charged negatively by mixing with larger (about 0.5-mm) carrier particles of glass or plastic-covered glass. The mixing charges the carrier particles positively and causes the toner particles to form a thin layer on the carrier particles, because of the attraction between the oppposite charges (Figure 8.8c). When these larger particles (toner plus carrier) are brought into contact with the zinc oxide, the negatively charged toner particles will stick to the positively charged areas, while the carrier particles fall off, and thus we have an (inverted) copy of the orginal object (Figure 8.8d).

The last step in the process consists of transferring the inverted picture to another surface, usually paper, as a noninverted copy. This can be done by bringing the (copy)paper into contact with the zinc oxide, while the back of the paper is grounded (Figure 8.8e). This will pull the toner particles onto the paper because of the attraction to a induced charge in the paper. Finally the paper is heated to fuse the toner particles to its surface, and we have the final copy. It should be stressed that the whole process is much more complicated than suggested here, and many of the subprocesses, like charging and development, may take place in completely different ways from those explained above.

5. Permanent Polarization, Electrets

It was mentioned earlier (see Chapter 2, Section 5) that a dielectric exposed to an electric field will be polarized. We can also state this by saying that the external field will be superimposed by a (dipole) field from the dielectric. Normally the polarization will relax and the field will disappear when the dielectric is removed from the external field. In certain materials, however, it is possible to maintain the polarization without the presence of an external field. Such a permanently polarized material is called an **electret**. The methods for the actual polarization or charging of electret materials will not be treated here, but we will discuss the properties and a few applications of electrets.

A practical electret will often be a thin (maybe 20–100 μm) sheet of, for instance, Teflon (polytetrafluorethylene) backed by an aluminum foil.

In Figure 8.9 is shown an electret of thickness d and relative permittivity ε_r. The backing foil is grounded and the electret is polarized (charged) with a surface density σ. The distance to the grounded surroundings assumed to be much larger than d. The field strength inside the electret is then

$$E_e = \frac{\sigma}{\varepsilon_0 \varepsilon_r} \tag{8.1}$$

The field on the free side of the electret is negligible because the distance to ground through the air is much larger than the thickness of the electret. The electret will have a surface potential

$$V_s = E_e d = \frac{\sigma d}{\varepsilon_0 \varepsilon_r} \tag{8.2}$$

If the distance to grounded surroundings is of the same order of magnitude as the thickness of the electret, the conditions are somewhat more complicated.

Figure 8.10 shows a grounded counter electrode parallel with the electret at a distance x from the charged surface. The electric field E_x in the air can now be written

$$E_x = \frac{\sigma}{\varepsilon_0 \left[\varepsilon_r \dfrac{x}{d} + 1 \right]} \tag{8.3}$$

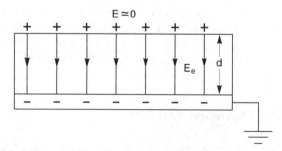

Figure 8.9 Charged electret

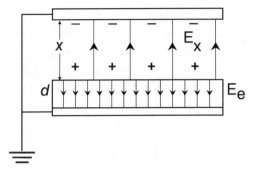

Figure 8.10 Electret with counter electrode

and the surface potential is

$$V_s = E_x x = \frac{\sigma d}{\varepsilon_0 \left[\varepsilon_r + \dfrac{d}{x} \right]} \tag{8.4}$$

Most applications of electrets are based on the utilization of the effect of the external field, as given by equation (8.3).

Radiological Exposuremeter

If an electret of the type shown in Figure 8.10 is placed in a location where radioactive gases (normally radon) create an (essential) ionization in the air, the field E_x will make (negative) ions move to the charged surface and cause the surface potential V_s to decrease with a rate proportional to the ionization rate and hence, under given radioactive conditions, to the radioactive exposure. The surface potential is measured by a field meter through an opening in the counter electrode. Although the device measures the exposure, it is often erroneously called a dosemeter.

Electret Microphone

One of the most important applications of electrets is as the active element in sensitive microphones (see Figure 8.11).

The counter electrode is a porous metal plate at a distance x from a membrane, consisting of the charged electret sheet. The counter electrode is connected to ground through a resistor of resistance R. When the membrane is at rest, the potential of the counter electrode is zero, and the field strength E_x is given by

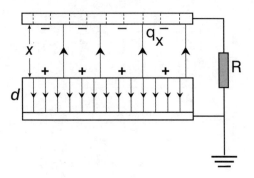

Figure 8.11 Electret microphone

equation (8.3). If the area of the counter electrode is A, a charge q_x is bound on the electrode and, according to equation (2.10), is given by

$$q_x = A\varepsilon_0 E_x = A\sigma \frac{d}{\varepsilon_r x + d} \tag{8.5}$$

The polarity of q_x is opposite that of σ.

If now the membrane is brought to oscillate, for instance, by being hit by a sound wave, the distance x and thus the charge q_x will vary with time. Let us assume that

$$x = x_0 + a \sin \omega t \tag{8.6}$$

and that the amplitude $a \ll x_0$. The charge q_x will thus vary with time, and through R will flow a current I_x given by

$$I_x = \frac{dq_x}{dt} = (-)\frac{A\sigma d\varepsilon_r a\omega}{(\varepsilon_r x + d)^2} \cos \omega t \simeq I_0 \cos \omega t \tag{8.7}$$

where the amplitude I_0 of the current is given by

$$I_0 = \frac{A\sigma d\varepsilon_r a\omega}{(\varepsilon_r x_0 + d)^2} \tag{8.8}$$

Across the resistor R will appear an alternating voltage of amplitude

$$V_0 = I_0 R \tag{8.9}$$

and this voltage may be amplified in a conventional way.

It appears that the microphone works without any external voltage supply, and it is believed that the electret will easily remain active as long as the rest of the microphone is in working condition.

Appendix A

Twelve Critical Factors in ESD Program Management*

Developing, implementing, and managing a successful ESD program requires a total system approach that extends from product design to customer acceptance. The program will need to be well managed and woven into every aspect of the manufacturing process in order to produce lasting success. In fact, *a well-managed program can be far more effective than one well stocked with expensive supplies*. The twelve critical factors described in this chapter (Table A-1) form the basis of successful ESD program management.

The first four factors listed in this chapter give the project its much needed organization and authority during the start-up and implementation phase, as well as afterwards during the long-term continual-improvement phase. These factors consist of a written implementation plan, management commitment, a full-time coordinator, and an active ESD committee. The next five factors described are the coordinator's essential tools: realistic requirements, a training program, an auditing program, a test lab, and an extensive communication effort. The three remaining factors are management principles that will help the program run more efficiently. These are systemic planning, human factors engineering, and continuous improvement.

The ESD coordinator must be aware of the twelve critical factors and fully understand their significance. *The factors need to be managed by the coordinator just as actively as the controls to protect sensitive devices and assemblies.* Sound management of these factors will produce a cost-effective program and sustained success.

Think of this chapter as an introduction to the twelve critical factors. By highlighting them in advance and out of context, they can be carried in the back of one's mind somewhat like a mental checklist. While some factors will stand out

* This Appendix has been reprinted with permission from G.T. Dangelmayer, ESD Program Management, Chapman and Hall, NY, 1990.

Table A.1 The Twelve Critical Factors for Successful ESD
Program Management

Factor One	An Effective Implementation Plan
Factor Two	Management Commitment
Factor Three	A Full-Time Coordinator
Factor Four	An Active Committee
Factor Five	Realistic Requirements
Factor Six	Training for Measurable Goals
Factor Seven	Auditing Using Scientific Measures
Factor Eight	ESD Test Facilities
Factor Nine	A Communication Program
Factor Ten	Systemic Planning
Factor Eleven	Human Factors Engineering
Factor Twelve	Continuous Improvement

more than others because they are given separate chapters, all are very important. Each one is woven into the fabric of the ESD control program, so each will be found in various contexts throughout the book. They are very important ideas, central to successful ESD program management. It can be very useful to return to this chapter repeatedly while studying the book, implementing a program, or evaluating the status of an ongoing program.

The Twelve Critical Factors

Factor One—An Effective Implementation Plan

The success of an ESD program depends on how well it is implemented. The best of programs can fail in the absence of a sound implementation plan. Therefore, it is critically important to develop an effective implementation plan in writing. Begin by developing a thorough understanding of the concepts in this book. Be sure that the outline of the implementation plan reflects the intent of the chapters that follow. The details of the plan should then be written down in the form of an action plan, to document individual responsibilities, deadlines, and progress. When finished, it will organize the massive undertaking of implementing a new or examining an ongoing program into a series of smaller projects, as well as give a first approximation of the work schedule. Be sure to include suppliers, distributors, and subcontractors when developing the plan because they are extensions of the program and must comply with its particulars. In fact, these companies should be chosen based on verifiable compliance with proper ESD procedures and approved packaging materials.

The plan is built around the other eleven factors described in this chapter and the steps described in Appendix B. As the reader studies this book, talks with members of the ESD committee, and surveys the manufacturing plant, details to the plan should be inserted under the appropriate category such as management commitment, a test lab, purchasing, automation, and so on. With each entry, the coordinator should include thoughts on who will work on each task and when.

By organizing the implementation effort in this way, the coordinator can see the larger picture and be less apt to get mired in details. Priorities can be set more effectively, tasks can be delegated to appropriate coworkers, and the timing of events can be regulated with an eye to how well employees are progressing with the programs.

Factor Two—Management Commitment

ESD control transcends the entire company, its suppliers, and subcontractors. Therefore, it is critically important to have support from all levels of management, especially from the top levels. In this way, a coordinated effort can be established swiftly and efficiently to implement the details of the plan. Otherwise, the numerous roadblocks that can develop along the way will become insurmountable and the program will fail.

Consequently, *management commitment must be actively sought* and then periodically reaffirmed for the program to succeed in the long run. In a large plant, there might be two or three hundred managers working in different capacities in the organizational hierarchy. A small plant, however, might have only two or three managers. In either case, managers at all levels who have authority over employees and have commitment to the ESD solution are a major part of the program's success. Without a clear and strong commitment early on from top management, there can be no long-term effort at solving the problem. Even if a few middle- or lower-level managers drag their feet at first, they will join the effort fairly quickly if they see that top management believes strongly in the program.

Once the commitment has been established, it should become common knowledge to all employees. It should be visible in the form of a signed statement describing the company's program to prevent ESD damage to devices and the nature of the ESD solution. It helps if management reissues this statement every year. Also, evidence of management commitment is seen when there is a budget to implement items such as training, purchasing, auditing, and so on. Included in this budget must be the money for a full-time coordinator.

Factor Three—A Full-Time Coordinator

Successfully implementing the ESD program requires a full-time effort by a well-qualified professional. This is a critical element, especially in the early stages.

Later on, a part-time effort may be sufficient in smaller companies. However, in large companies the task cannot be done effectively on a part-time basis. Studying the technology, selecting and purchasing the needed equipment, preparing the procedures handbook and manuals, building a training program, and putting the critical factors into place are no trivial task. The problem is compounded by the fact that very few engineers understand the technology, and even fewer understand the risks. The ESD coordinator must serve as a consultant to all of the engineering disciplines in addition to overseeing the plan. Implementing an effective ESD management program requires a dedicated effort to reap the financial benefits.

The ESD coordinator should be a member of the quality organization. In this way, the program becomes a global responsibility transcending all manufacturing and engineering organizations and touching the entire manufacturing work flow from design to the finished product. Figure A.1 illustrates a typical manufacturing flowchart that includes ESD considerations and extends from design to customer acceptance. As a member of quality control, the coordinator will have the necessary support and tools to easily affect the entire manufacturing process and business entity. The coordinator will understand and be able to use the concepts of statistical quality control to manage the ESD program. These concepts will make it possible to recognize when a systemic change is needed or if a specific cause is responsible for current problems. These techniques are also an integral part of the auditing program.

A well-qualified coordinator should understand quality control engineering as well as have a strong technical background in order to master ESD technology. ESD control is a new field, which needs to be learned by the work force. Therefore, the coordinator must also be an effective communicator and a good teacher. Also, since it is a new field, there are many problems that demand creative engineering. Other qualifications needed for the job are common sense and initiative.

Managing the program and serving as an authoritative ESD consultant to the entire company are the major responsibilities of the coordinator. This is how continual improvement happens. To manage the program, the coordinator must identify problems and solve them. This can be done by overseeing auditing, using data to pinpoint problems, delegating resources such as training, reporting and making proposals to management, directing purchasing, directing the efforts of the ESD committee, preparing training documentation, and using every possible means to keep management and the work force informed.

Factor Four—An Active Committee

An active ESD control committee will unify the effort and help solve problems more efficiently. The committee is a critical factor because even a full-time coordinator cannot implement or upgrade the program alone; the task is too great and affects too many disciplines. A working committee that shares information and

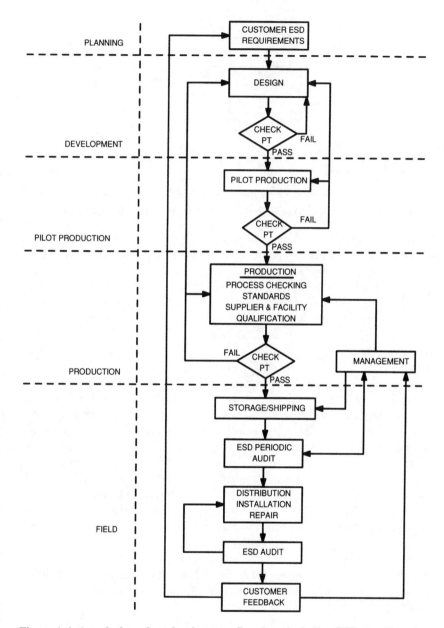

Figure A.1 A typical product development flowchart including ESD considerations

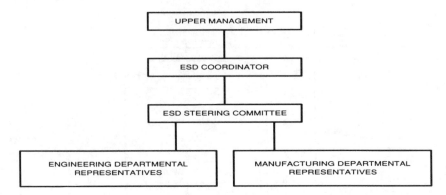

Figure A.2 Local ESD control committee organizational flowchart

enlists help from many experts and managers is an invaluable resource for the coordinator. It is a vital part of the communication process and results in an appropriate sharing of responsibility.

At AT&T manufacturing locations, we have two subcommittees (Figure A.2): engineering departmental representatives and manufacturing departmental representatives. The engineering representatives are the personnel with the requisite knowledge and skills for solving ESD problems. They include packaging engineers, test engineers, an ergonomic expert, trainers, safety representatives, product engineers, and process engineers. The manufacturing representatives consist primarily of shop supervisors who coordinate the ESD effort in their department.

In general, the committee is responsible for developing policies and procedures. These responsibilities include promoting ESD awareness and control, ensuring local compliance with ESD instructions, identifying and resolving ESD issues, and maintaining a team of local ESD specialists to assist in solving related problems.

Large corporations with more than one manufacturing and assembly plant should also have a corporate committee to unify the company's efforts across plant boundaries. Figure A.3 shows how this committee is staffed and organized at AT&T. It includes both manufacturing and research and development (R&D). Led by cochairpersons, subgroups include communications, control procedures and documentation, standards, consultants, and R&D.

The corporate committee is an effective means of sharing solutions to common problems and minimizing redundant effort. This approach provides a constancy of purpose that makes it possible to develop consensus standards and establish a unified approach to the needs of the corporation.

Factor Five—Realistic Requirements

The ESD control requirements must be realistic and formally documented, for they are the foundation of the entire plan (see Chapter 7, "Realistic Require-

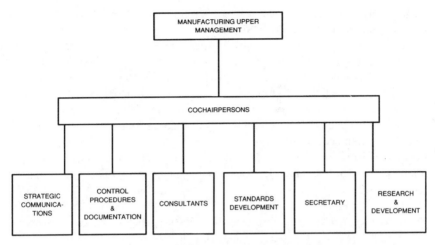

Figure A.3 Corporate ESD control organizational flowchart

ments"). All activities, procedures, and support documents are based on these requirements. It is, therefore, critically important for the requirements to be well documented in easy-to-understand language and mindful of training needs. Consistent compliance with proper procedures depends on a complete understanding of the requirements; thus, thorough documentation is essential. Furthermore, the requirements must be realistic to be enforceable.

Written as a handbook, the requirements can also serve as a text during training and as a common reference for all employees. The information in the handbook is then a comprehensive statement of the ESD control program. Training is based on it, the auditing checklist is written to ensure compliance with it, and the employee's work is structured from it.

Although the requirements are extensive and complete, they must also be realistic so that people can follow them easily. They must be *written in such a way that human error is improbable*. This is accomplished by explaining procedures clearly and by placing a high priority on human factors engineering (Factor Eleven) whenever possible.

In addition, support manuals should be written for activities such as process checking, auditing, and maintaining facilities. These documents should also be comprehensive and realistic.

Factor Six—Training for Measurable Goals

Training is an obviously critical factor in successful ESD control and must be a primary consideration at all times. A training program built on measurable goals derived from the auditing program allows the coordinator to aggressively pursue the identification and resolution of training needs. The auditing results clearly identify when training is needed, who needs training, what needs to be taught, and whether the training was successful.

Special emphasis should be placed on training engineers, maintenance technicians, and first-line supervisors. Given their involvement and highly visible positions, these people must set an example for others to follow. Instead, they are often the worst violators of proper ESD procedures and undermine the programs in an unconscious manner. A sound training program can correct this situation.

During the development and scheduling of training courses, it is vitally important to take into account the Three Principles of the Psychology of Training and Learning. Using them as a guide will greatly enhance the effectiveness of the training program. These principles are discussed in more detail in Chapter 11 and are listed below:

Principle One: Train students only in order to affect a measurable change in work behavior.

Principle Two: Motivate students to improve learning.

Principle Three: Take into consideration the fact that students tend to forget information and skills not used regularly.

Factor Seven—Auditing Using Scientific Measures

Auditing is the binding force behind a sound program and is critical to a program's long-term success. Its mere presence spurs compliance and a strong management commitment that fosters continuous improvement. Published reports can motivate managers and engineers towards improving the program in their department.

The reports provide the coordinator with the tools necessary to effectively manage and maintain the program. They make it possible to easily identify problems and then solve them. Chapter 8, "Implementing an Auditing Program," and Chapter 9, "Using Auditing Results to Manage the ESD Program," provide examples of how major problems can be identified and permanently resolved.

The selection of the auditor (see Chapter 8) is critical. This person must be able to withstand peer pressure and to report all deviations as initially detected. The objective is to protect sensitive products from ESD damage by supplying management with valid information that can be used for swift corrective action.

Using statistical sampling techniques, auditing measures departmental compliance with the prescribed ESD control procedures. These are the procedures from the handbook and the manuals that employees are trained to follow. The statistical unit of measure for the program is the deviation from prescribed procedure.

The procedures are transformed into a questionnaire type of checklist. In addition to this checklist, the auditing program consists of an auditing inspector, a manual, a portable test cart, and software for filing and organizing data. The collected data is printed in graph form as either a trend chart or a Pareto analysis. The coordinator uses these graphs to spot trends, identify and pinpoint problems, and report progress to management. As stated above, these reports are also an invaluable training tool. The net result of an auditing program is continual improvement.

Factor Eight—ESD Test Facilities

Having adequate testing capability is a critical tool for the coordinator. It allows the coordinator to use electrical tests to scientifically evaluate many aspects of the program and its success. For instance, testing is an integral part of such activities as auditing, qualifying equipment and sensitive components for purchase, defining effective requirements and procedures, inspecting incoming control products, solving manufacturing problems, providing failure mode analysis on devices and systems, demonstrating during training, and testing and qualifying devices or systems prior to shipment.

While some testing can be very sophisticated, much of the testing recommended in this book is basic. This is in keeping with the program's philosophy of being realistic. For instance, by testing and qualifying ESD control equipment, greater standardization of the auditing test procedures can be achieved. In fact, the program at AT&T is set up so that all of the periodic requalification tests done by manufacturing process checkers can be accomplished with a wrist strap tester. This one idea lowers maintenance costs considerably, makes the test easier to perform, and simplifies training. (See Chapter 10 for more details.)

The test facilities on hand will depend on one's budget, plant size, and testing goals. Chapter 6 describes a variety of test equipment and one method of setting up three types of testing facilities, such as a field audit kit that fits in a suitcase, a general lab that includes a portable test cart, and an analytic/failure mode analysis (FMA) laboratory.

Factor Nine—A Communication Program

Effective communication is a vital element in successful ESD control and is *one of the most challenging critical factors*. Coordinators often underestimate the difficulty or fail to recognize the importance of establishing a communication program. A sound communication program must be developed at the outset and actively managed at all times. For instance, a quality auditor once asked why a certain requirement had changed three times in nine months. In reality, the requirement had been published three years earlier and had never been changed; it was merely the auditor's understanding that changed. This is typical of the immense difficulties associated with effective communication.

Therefore, the coordinator should take advantage of every available channel of communication, take advantage of every opportunity to keep people aware of the ESD problem, demonstrate that progress is being made towards its solution, and post quality improvement charts and graphs where all can view them. It should be assumed that people need to know. What might seem obvious to a coordinator, such as how to test a bench top or adjust a wrist strap, is not necessarily obvious to others.

Examples of communication possibilities include publicizing the fact that a department had zero deviations or sending an ESD bulletin when a new type of wrist strap is to be used. Information about the ESD control program should be included in the introductory materials for new employees. Publish a policy statement annually. Invite the local press to visit a class or a training demonstration. Give reports frequently to management, both in writing and verbally, during business results meetings. Coordinators should be able to find many additional ways of communicating with all involved parties.

Most plants have all of the necessary channels of communication available. These include signs, posters, bulletins, video displays, a public address system, classrooms and meeting rooms, capabilities for publishing handbooks and manuals, supervisors, quality process checkers or their equivalent, a newsletter, interoffice mail for memos and letters, and electronic mail. Less common and very effective is a Quality Fair (See Chapter 11, "Training for Measurable Goals.")

Factor Ten—Systemic Planning

The diverse elements of an ESD control program form a total system that will ultimately determine the success of the program. It is critically important to realize that *each element is part of an integrated whole* rather than separate distinct entities. A change in any part of the program will have a ripple effect on other elements. Conversely, there are times when the program must be changed to effect desired improvement. Therefore, systemic planning becomes yet another aspect of the program that requires constant awareness and management on the part of the coordinator.

First, by planning ahead for the ripple effect of a change, the coordinator can anticipate its total consequence. This will lessen confusion and prevent the creation of new problems while trying to solve an existing problem. For example, consider the implication of a relatively minor change in wrist straps in which you go from using three different sizes to using one adjustable wrist strap. That single change should prompt the following questions. Will people need additional training in how to adjust the new strap? Must the section on wrist straps in the handbook be rewritten? Does this change affect the inspector's manual or checklist? What is the most effective way to communicate this change? Can the new wrist strap be tested in the same manner as the ones being replaced? Must new test equipment be purchased? If a new test is warranted, what written documents must be changed? Will one adjustable wrist band really fit everybody? Will employees find the wrist straps comfortable and safe? Should there be backup wrist straps for very small or very large people? Can the new wrist strap be purchased without changing our long-term relationship with the current wrist strap vendor?

Secondly, the ripple effect in an integrated program often masks the root cause of a problem. Not finding the root cause in a program will mean facing the same problem again and again.

For example, auditing uncovered a problem with heelstraps. Further study revealed that many employees were wearing them incorrectly. The obvious solution would have been additional training. However, due to the complicated nature of the heelstrap, the training problem would have been endless. The root cause of the problem was really in the design of the heelstrap and not in the training methods. After the heelstrap was replaced with a simplified version, human error became improbable and the problem was permanently solved. See Chapter 9, "Using Auditing Results to Manage the ESD Program," for additional examples.

Factor Eleven—Human Factors Engineering

The employees' ability to comply with the ESD control procedures is a major part of the ESD solution. Every aspect of the program that affects people must be engineered in such a way that all reasonable employee needs and desires are taken care of and that human error is improbable. For example, if the equipment is uncomfortable or inconvenient, employees will be less apt to comply with the procedures. In fact, failure to consider their needs could cause a catastrophic breakdown in the program. Considering their needs through human factors engineering is also a critical factor, one which must be examined in all aspects of the program.

Asking different pilot groups of employees to trial-test all equipment and procedures is a primary technique of human factors engineering. This helps the coordinator understand employees' needs and builds a body of knowledge on effective solutions. For example, trial testing revealed that some types of wrist strap materials produced a rash on some employees. This discovery avoided a serious problem.

Our experience with trial-testing has proven to us that employees want to do their jobs well, which includes complying with procedures. Giving employees a say on matters concerning convenience and safety, whether it be a choice of color or the best length for wrist strap cords, costs little and will reap great rewards.

Factor Twelve—Continuous Improvement

Continuous improvement of each of the previous eleven critical factors is an essential part of a sound ESD control program. Implemented effectively, the critical factors will produce a cost-effective program. However, it is the continuous improvement of those factors that will sustain the success. Many companies, failing to recognize the importance of this, have undertaken control programs with enthusiasm only to let them deteriorate into a state of disrepair and total ineffectiveness. Consequently, the funds expended for the program have been wasted and none of the quality improvements have been realized. Often the deficiencies go undetected because there is no auditing program in effect.

In contrast, the ultimate goal of ESD control and all other manufacturing quality control efforts must be satisfied customers through better products, services, and costs. This is not a fixed goal like winning a road race. Continual improvement is an endless process of meeting one goal after another.

Fixed goals are an important first approximation when working toward continual improvement. For the first 5 years, the primary goal should be to achieve zero deviations from prescribed ESD control procedures. This measurable goal allows for the setting of priorities, putting the coordinator in charge of tackling the most serious problem first, the next serious problem second, and so on. It also provides a straightforward way to report results. Chapter 9, "Using Auditing Results to Manage the ESD Program," describes this technique in a detailed way.

But what happens when there are zero deviations in the program? Is the project a success? Is the project completed? No! The project will have accomplished a monumental achievement when zero deviations are achieved and sustained. The project should not, however, be considered completed. There is always room for further improvement. No matter how good we are today, we can and must be even better tomorrow. Furthermore, *failure to continuously improve the process will translate into complacency and deterioration.*

There are always better and more cost-effective techniques, new control products to evaluate, new solutions to consider, and better training techniques to incorporate. Add to this the trend toward devices of ever increasing sensitivity to ESD damage. Staying abreast of the technology becomes vital. Later chapters illustrate the extreme technical difficulties that these ultrasensitive devices present as well as the need to be prepared for them.

Points To Remember

- The twelve critical factors form the basis for successful ESD program management.
- The twelve critical factors should be kept in mind when studying this book, implementing the program, and managing the ongoing program.
- The twelve critical factors should be used as categories when writing the implementation plan. The plan should be written as an action plan.
- Management commitment should be obtained at all levels and periodically reenforced.
- The nature and massive scope of the project requires a full-time coordinator who is well qualified for the job.
- A local ESD control committee composed of both engineering specialists and manufacturing managers will enlist help from others and unify the effort.

- A written handbook consisting of realistic requirements is the backbone of the control program.
- A training program based on measurable goals teaches the awareness and skills necessary for employees to comply with procedures. The training program is based on the handbook.
- An auditing program using scientific measures is a binding force behind the whole program and fosters continual improvement.
- Adequate ESD test facilities make it possible for the coordinator to scientifically develop, manage, and direct the control program.
- An active communication program, maintained at all times, uses all available channels of communication to explain and publicize ESD control.
- Systemic planning is important. An integrated program such as ESD control can experience a ripple effect, where changes in one part of the program can ripple through other parts of the program, causing new problems or masking the root cause of a problem.
- Employees will comply with procedures more willingly when human factors engineering is incorporated. The goal is to engineer solutions in such a way that human error is improbable.
- A primary goal of the ESD control program is continuous improvement through continual attention to the twelve critical factors. An important interim goal is zero deviations. The ultimate goal must be satisfied customers.

Appendix B

Implementing an ESD Control Program: The Basic Steps*

The 16 basic steps introduced in this chapter will provide the basis for the design and implementation of effective ESD program management. Presenting the steps first in this chapter in a brief outline offers a conceptual overview before focusing on individual steps in later chapters. This is especially beneficial for manufacturing companies contemplating the organization of such a program or for those attempting to strengthen their commitment to controlling ESD.

Following these 16 steps in the order in which they are presented will help foster two of the key elements of any successful companywide program: commitment and communication. (See Appendix A for more details.) The 16 steps are designed to secure, from the start, a top-down commitment to the program. Later steps will involve middle and lower levels of management and, finally, all members of the work force. As each department in the organization enlists in the ESD program, a strong sense of program ownership will emerge. The result should be a measurable improvement in performance, not only in that department, but throughout the entire organization.

Good communication is vital to the smooth implementation of an effective program. Communication ensures that top management remains involved in the program's development and deployment and allows all responsible personnel, throughout the organization, to follow the program's progress. Ongoing communication enables everyone to share in a successful implementation and to contribute to future improvements in the program. In addition, continued communication, over time, enables individual operating departments to revise their own goals, to learn from the progress in other departments, and to share in the discovery of new technologies and new testing procedures. In short, commu-

---

* This Appendix has been reprinted with permission from G.T. Dangelmayer, ESD Program Management, Chapman and Hall, NY, 1990.

nication helps everyone responsible for ESD control to participate in the continuous improvement of the organization's program.

The Basic Steps

Step 1: Study and Understand the Technology of ESD Control

When strengthening an existing program or before an effective program of ESD control can be developed, it is absolutely essential for the ESD coordinator to acquire a thorough understanding of the physics and engineering involved in the control of ESD. This will permit the establishment of effective requirements, realistic goals, and a program of control specifically designed for each facility.

A thorough understanding of the ESD technology will make it possible to develop cost-effective solutions for specific handling requirements. In addition, this understanding assures that solutions will be technically sound and will provide the required level of protection without incurring an unreasonable level of expense. In short, this knowledge will help avoid what might otherwise be overprotective insurance.

Developing a worthwhile training program, one that will contribute to the ESD control program's continued success, also requires a thorough understanding of the technology of the problem and its possible solutions. The training itself is valid, and valuable, only if it is based on sound technology. If employees can see through a weak technological argument, then they will question every step the program demands that they take.

It is especially important that the facility's ESD coordinator share this thorough understanding of ESD technology. The coordinator must be perceived as a credible authority on all aspects of the problem and its solution. Frequently, the coordinator will be required to answer a wide range of technical questions regarding the program. The ability to respond knowledgeably will help the coordinator more readily win acceptance among all employees and management. In turn, employee acceptance of the coordinator as a knowledgeable authority will contribute to smoother program implementation. This is especially true where ESD damage often occurs with no discernible sensation.

The first step in achieving the necessary level of understanding is to review the existing literature.[2.21] The proceedings of symposia sponsored by the EOS/ESD Association (an international organization) are a good place to begin. They include papers presented by companies such as AT&T Bell Laboratories, specific AT&T manufacturing locations, Bellcore, British Telecommunications, 3M, Honeywell, Texas Instruments, and other leaders in the field of ESD control technology.

A second step to understanding ESD technology might be to attend the EOS/ESD Symposium. EOS/ESD symposia provide one of the best forums for the presentation and discussion of timely information on the state of ESD control technology. Attending tutorials is also helpful in learning about advances in the control of ESD. There are many tutorials from which to choose, including those offered at the EOS/ESD Symposia.

These symposia and forums also offer access to professional ESD consultants who may be available to provide assistance in developing or upgrading a customized control program. It is particularly important that any consultant hired to develop such a program have substantial experience in implementation.

Every company planning to implement an ESD control program or strengthening an existing program should join the EOS/ESD Association. As a member, the ESD coordinator will be able to find help in identifying qualified consultants. Attendance at EOS/ESD events will lead to familiarity with other leading authorities in the field whose expertise may prove helpful at a later date. Some locations in the United States now have local chapter meetings of the EOS/ESD Association, another valuable opportunity to acquire ESD knowledge at little cost.

Step 2: Gather Scientific Evidence of the Economic Value of ESD Control

One of the most important steps in gaining or strengthening management commitment for the development or upgrading of the ESD program is the establishment of the program's short- and long-term economic benefits. Gathering the scientific evidence to support these benefits will also yield an even deeper understanding of the technology. Additional knowledge can be gained through participation in scientific experiments designed to demonstrate the benefits of ESD control. The experiments should include pilot studies in designated areas so that yield improvements can be documented. Experiments of this kind are discussed more fully in Chapter 4, "An Economic Analysis."

There is a wealth of literature available that focuses on the economic benefits of ESD control programs. For example, the EOS/ESD Association has recently published *An ESD Management Focus*,[22] a collection of selected papers from the first decade of EOS/ESD Symposia. These papers describe control programs, their economic value, and the training programs associated with them.

The information gathered in this way will allow for a preliminary estimate of the savings to be generated by your facility's ESD program. This estimate may be updated as additional information becomes available. Publishing preliminary findings and issuing subsequent updates may help solidify needed management support for the program.

Step 3: Establish an Active ESD Committee

Assuring the success of an ESD control program is work for more than one person. In order for the program to succeed, the ESD coordinator will need the assistance of an active committee.

This committee should include representatives from all of the key functions within the facility such as training, safety, engineering, operations, manufacturing, packaging, purchasing, and personnel.

The committee's task should be to help plan and implement each of the steps outlined in this chapter, and described more fully in this book. Of course, these steps are only a guide to ESD program development or expansion. The steps adopted by the committee should be tailored to fit the specific conditions of each manufacturing facility.

Once the committee has been established, it is important that specific responsibilities be assigned to each member. *The coordinator cannot plan and implement a complete program alone.*

At first, the committee should meet as frequently as once a week. Reports of each week's meetings should be distributed to key management people responsible for implementation. Frequent reports of the committee's progress will help prepare the ground work necessary to win management's long-term commitment to the program.

Additional details of committee functions and responsibilities were presented in Appendix A, "Twelve Critical Factors in ESD Program Management."

Step 4: Develop a General Implementation Plan

Once the ESD committee is in place, the next step is the development of a comprehensive implementation plan. Special emphasis should be placed on gathering and organizing the information necessary to secure top management support. Because *any one aspect of the plan will affect all others*, it is essential that an exhaustive program for ESD control be developed at once.

One of the first steps in plan development is the identification of ESD sensitive areas and the engineers who share responsibility for those areas. As a second step, an action plan (including goals and an implementation schedule) can be prepared for each area simultaneously.

Manufacturing areas must be carefully surveyed and their ESD control implementation needs identified in thorough detail. This survey will provide a basis for estimating the actual implementation costs and for projecting the rate of return on investment to be delivered by the ESD control program. This information will be necessary to help establish top management commitment and the funding necessary for implementation .

Step 5: Write or Adopt a Set of Realistic Handling Requirements

It is vitally important to formally document and distribute the handling requirements for each manufacturing facility at the onset of implementation. These requirements need to be based on a thorough understanding of ESD technology, as described in Steps 1 and 2. They must take into account the level of training required for each manufacturing operation. The requirements must also reflect an understanding of human nature and must realistically address employee attitudes.

Handling requirements may vary with device sensitivity. Yet, it is frequently impractical to train all employees in the many different ways that devices of differing sensitivity must be handled. Instead, consideration should be given to organizing work areas in the plant based upon device sensitivity, such that employee training will be consistent throughout each work area. Each area should be equipped to protect the most sensitive device that will be handled there. Install the equipment and train all employees in an area to use the equipment installed in that area. Thus, the equipment provided will introduce added protection for the more sensitive devices, and the degree of training will be the same in each area. This kind of engineering solution will maximize the value of employee training. Additional information on training requirements can be found in Chapter 11, "Training for Measurable Goals."

Document all handling requirements before attempting to gain a broad management commitment. Once that commitment has been given, implementation will move rapidly and the handling requirements documentation will be required for consistent compliance with ESD control procedures. The documentation will also provide a valuable platform for good communication within the work force. Distribute the handling requirements to all employees immediately after gaining management commitment for the project.

Step 6: Prepare a Detailed Statement of Policy Including Individual Responsibilities

The company's corporate ESD policy statement should clearly stipulate the intention to control ESD in all operating environments. The policy should also *include a clear definition of responsibility* for every individual in the enterprise, from top management to all employees. See Appendix 1, "AT&T ESD Policy" for an example.

To ensure that the statement will be read by the widest possible audience, make certain that the entire statement fits on a single typewritten page. Plan to post the statement in appropriate and prominent places throughout the company and to distribute it, individually, to management personnel.

Be sure to gain management's complete commitment to the policy prior to publication.

Step 7: Prepare a Presentation for Management

Management reports must be concise, direct, and to the point, or they will be ineffective and the opportunity to win top-down support may be lost. The information should be current and should be well organized. Plan on finalizing the presentation after a meeting with management has been scheduled. Until then, facts should be updated continuously so that a formal report can be quickly prepared for distribution.

Information to be presented in the report includes the economic analysis used to estimate the potential savings engendered by ESD control in Step 2. The results of any experiments that may have been conducted at the facility should be included. Use these figures to estimate the return on investment through increased yields due to reduced static (ESD) induced failures during manufacturing.

The results of the literature search should be paraphrased and presented in a concise format so that management may observe trends in technology and implementation. This information should also be presented in such a way as to demonstrate the relevancy of the scientific literature to the facility for which the new or expanded ESD control program is intended.

The report should also include a reminder of the technological trend toward devices of ever increasing sensitivity. Even if no major problems are apparent in the facility today, as devices become more sensitive, problems are sure to occur.

A discussion of the intangible benefits that the program promises to deliver should also be included. They can be of great importance. As discussed in Chapter 14, "Payback and Benefits," one important intangible benefit of ESD control is a significant improvement in customer satisfaction.

The presentation should also include a brief synopsis of the proposed implementation plan and a systematic approach to the problem. Other obviously essential elements of the presentation are a proposed policy statement and a copy of the handling requirements.

Ask that management become involved at once and conclude with a clearly stated request for the desired commitment. That commitment is, after all, essential to the program's success. The report should recommend that the coordinator be appointed on a full-time basis to launch the program successfully. It can also be mentioned that in later years, depending on the size of the facility or company, it may not be necessary to maintain this as a full-time position. This appointment of a full-time coordinator is the first test of management's commitment to the success of the ESD control program.

Step 8: Establish a Top Management Commitment

As soon as a thorough, systematic, well coordinated program and presentation have been developed, the next essential detail is to request an opportunity to present the case as soon as it is practical to do so to top management. Prompt action is critical to the long-term success of the program.

When a program that involves the entire company is instituted, such as an ESD control program, the drive to implement and succeed must come from the top of the organization. The program is too important to the success of the company to be left to lower management. Effective ESD control requires the cooperation of every department, without regard to traditional areas of responsibility and "turf." In addition, the ESD coordinator must be able to cross conventional lines of report and responsibility with top management's freely granted blessings. Therefore, the initial management presentation should take place as early as possible in the development of the program in order to clear any roadblocks that may inadvertently arise along the way.

The importance of gaining the early and active support of top management cannot be overemphasized. Make the presentation concise and to the point. The developers must include a direct request for approval of the new policy and procedures.

Step 9: Develop the Details of ESD Program Management

Once top management commitment has been established, it is time to develop the management details of a new or expanded ESD program. Because damage caused by ESD is both insidious and often undiscernible when it occurs, it is necessary to develop a coordinated control plan for purchasing, training, manufacturing, and shipping. In fact, a systematic approach to *ESD control must extend from the initial design of the product through customer acceptance*. To achieve this virtual blanket of protection, the plan for all areas must be fully integrated.

This comprehensive approach requires that the actual conditions present within the organization and its suppliers be considered before the onset of implementation. Among the necessary steps that should be taken are the following:

- Select suppliers of sensitive devices and assemblies based on their ESD control program, the design of their products, and their protective packaging for shipment. Test methods for qualifying product design are described in Chapter 5, "Designed-In Protection and Product Testing." A supplier's control program should meet or exceed the standards set in this book. See Chapter 9 for an example of how to audit subcontractors or suppliers.

- Purchase ESD control equipment based on a thorough understanding of ESD control requirements. A purchasing plan should be instituted that is fully coordinated with all other aspects of the program (see Chapter 10, "Purchasing Guidelines: Finding the Hidden Costs and Problems"). Equipment specifications should always include training considerations and documentation implications.

- Establish and maintain, on-site, a test laboratory. The lab is required for the regular analysis of all items purchased, as well as for a thorough understanding of handling requirements and new ESD control technology. (See Chapter 6, "ESD Test Facilities.")

- Develop a customized training program that takes into account how people in the operation actually do their jobs. Ongoing training, for all levels of the work force, is essential in order to instill safe and proper work habits. (See Chapter 11, "Training for Measurable Goals.")

- Develop a quality control plan to ensure day-to-day compliance. It is vitally important that this plan include statistical sampling in the manufacturing area. In that way, the program will allow for timely verification that the intended procedures are being followed. (See Chapter 8, "Implementing an Auditing Program," and Chapter 9, "Using Auditing Results to Manage the ESD Program.")

Above all, for any plan to succeed, there must be a facilitywide commitment to strive for continuous improvement.

Step 10: Present the Program to Middle and Lower Management

The next phase in implementation is to expand the presentation of the program goals and practices to include middle and lower management. Reaching out to these management levels is the first step in developing broad, cross-departmental support for the program.

The middle management presentation is an opportunity to explain the details of the program to those who are going to be most directly responsible for the program's success. This presentation is the first forum in which to define and explain individual responsibilities. At the same time, the presentation offers a good opportunity to emphasize the need for a total team effort.

The ESD coordinator cannot successfully manage a comprehensive control program alone. He/she will need to *delegate many of the responsibilities* to different individuals. Clearly the success of that delegation requires selecting people whose primary responsibilities assure their involvement with ESD control.

For example, if engineering is responsible for providing the machinery for any given operation, then the same engineers should be responsible for providing the

ESD control functions for that operation. If manufacturing is responsible for providing its own facilities, then that department should also be responsible for purchasing and maintaining the ESD control facilities used within that manufacturing environment. This is a highly effective way to delegate responsibility and to foster department by department ownership of a corporatewide program.

ESD is a major part of everyone's responsibility, much like safety. Delegating specific responsibilities is both necessary and reasonable, but requires management support. Details of the coordinator's responsibilities were discussed in Appendix A, "Twelve Critical Factors in ESD Program Management."

Step 11: Begin Implementation of the Control Facilities

Once the details of the program have been laid out, management has been informed, and all participating departments have been assigned their ESD control responsibilities, the primary activity of the ESD control committee then becomes coordinating the implementation of control facilities such as wrist straps, grounded workstations, and dissipative tote trays.

The action plan that was developed earlier (see Step 4) can now be used to expedite implementation, by identifying critical items and making sure that they are implemented in a timely fashion. Following the action plan closely will help ensure that all implementation activities are coordinated for optimal efficiency.

Prepare and distribute status reports to the appropriate management levels on a regular basis. This will serve to keep them up-to-date on facility implementation throughout the corporation. Periodic reporting will also help to maintain the necessary emphasis on the project.

It is absolutely essential that *savings realized at each stage of implementing the control procedures be fully documented as they are achieved*. This step is too often overlooked, even though clearly documented savings will maintain vital management interest in the project. As the savings promised by the program's earlier projections are actually realized, support among department heads will grow. At the same time, management's commitment, established when the project began, will find a continued basis for reinforcement.

Now is also the right time to begin awareness training, as described in Chapter 9. Awareness training should focus on both individual employees and on management supervisors. In addition, awareness training should include a program of ongoing communications that maintains interest in and concern for ESD control throughout both plants and corporate offices.

As part of that timely communications effort, a copy of top management's signed ESD policy statement should be distributed throughout the organization. Reissue the statement annually, to ensure that everyone continues to understand the importance to the operation of controlling ESD.

Step 12: Begin Training of the Entire Work Force, Including Management

Once facilities are in place, actual hands-on training of the work force can begin. The most effective method used is to train in stages. Proper organization of training materials and lessons is the key to acceptance, retention, and active participation.

Provide employees with a thorough explanation of why ESD control is necessary. Describe how each specific control program helps to prevent damage from ESD. Be especially clear in pointing out how each individual can contribute to the success of the total ESD program. It is essential that all questions be answered and that any fears, however irrational, be laid to rest.

A key element in training is to be certain that employees understand how the systems and equipment work. Employees must know how to operate new systems and equipment before they are challenged by their use in actual daily operations. For example, the necessity of personnel grounding and the technology behind wrist straps and conductive footwear should be explained. Provide ample reassurance of the safety of these devices, and explain how safety resistors work to protect an employee. Employees are often surprised to find that these devices are actually safer than a direct touch to electrical ground procedures where there is no current limiting resistor present. To stimulate and maintain interest further, include lively demonstrations whenever possible.

To achieve the highest level of positive response from the trainees and to sustain the desired change in behavior, complete training before asking employees to use ESD control devices. At this stage in the program's implementation, the requirement is to reach as many people as possible, as quickly as possible. Therefore, mass training techniques are not only in order, they are recommended. Many of these training techniques are described in detail in Chapter 11, "Training for Measurable Goals."

Step 13: Begin Using Facilities Immediately After Training

With the proper ESD control facilities in place and training complete, employees will be able to use these facilities as soon as they return to their jobs. Any delay in the application of what they have learned can seriously impair the training program's effectiveness and reduce employee acceptance.

It is particularly important not to allow employees to persist in improper or inadequate performance, even if a shortage of ESD control facilities should develop. By permitting inappropriate behavior for any reason, management risks appearing to condone that behavior. Unfortunately, once a way of performing a task has been learned, unlearning it is extremely difficult. For example, if employees are allowed to touch ground when a wrist strap has not been installed or are permitted to hold PWB assemblies by their faceplates because wrist straps are unavailable, potentially damaging habits will result and will prove hard to eliminate even when the proper equipment is in place.

During this early stage in the implementation phase, *anticipate the need for on-the-job training*. Virtually every individual in the building will need some additional training, either from a management supervisor or from a professional trainer.

Consistency from the start is the key to training the work force. Always insist that the ESD program's documented requirements are followed to the letter. If employees are consistently unable to meet that standard of performance, consider whether the requirements might be unrealistic and need to be revised.

Step 14: Begin Formal Auditing of All Manufacturing Departments

After a 6-month grace period and a number of courtesy surveys have been completed, it is time to begin formal auditing of the progress in all departments.

Until all ESD control facilities have been installed and the basic work force training has been conducted, the ESD coordinator and several well trained engineers on the committee should conduct informal surveys of each operating site. In the course of these surveys, they should identify problem areas and classify them. Trouble spots can be grouped by the type of handling violation, with specific reference to either improperly trained employees or unacceptable facility installation.

A plan of corrective action for each area should be established, and the results entered as soon as they are available. This information should be shared informally with all involved departments, as well as with the representatives from engineering and manufacturing.

Meetings should be held to discuss whatever has been discovered in the course of the surveys. Open communication will help to gain the support of department personnel and will help them to develop a better understanding of the requirements. Then, when actual auditing begins, employees in each department will be better positioned to satisfy those requirements for handling procedures.

The experience gained during these surveys will also form the basis for more detailed auditing programs. These auditing programs will need to be enacted as the entire operation begins to follow the requirements of the ESD control program. Formal auditing can begin after the 6-month grace period. By then, most departments will have a thorough understanding of the program's requirements and procedures.

Step 15: Report Auditing Results, Graphically and With Regularity, to All Levels of Management

To ensure improvement, it is necessary to audit results carefully and consistently. Publication of the results will ensure that improvement is rapid as well.

Unfortunately, corporate decision makers often do not have time to read long reports; yet it is absolutely essential that management be kept up to date on the progress of the ESD control program throughout the operation. Continued top-down enthusiasm is needed if the program is to succeed over the long term.

Therefore, reports need to be short and to the point. Information must be presented graphically in order to highlight results such as comparisons of work force behavior and departmental performance. Graphic representations of this kind of information can instantly demonstrate the state of ESD control within the corporation.

Reports that are easy to read and convey information at a glance will inspire management to react to situations quickly and more effectively. *Distribute these reports to all levels of management* in order to maintain essential emphasis on the program goals and performance. Only if both top and middle management are kept informed of necessary adjustments to the program will appropriate corrective action be taken in a timely fashion. To that end, reports should be issued monthly or with each audit of every department.

Graphs showing quality improvement can also be displayed where the direct labor work force can see them. This will aid in enlisting universal support for the ESD program.

Step 16: Continuously Improve the Process

New, improved, and more cost-effective solutions to the problems of ESD related damage are continuously being developed and tested. To take advantage of innovative technology requires an open mind and a dedication to continued investigation and analysis. It is important not only to stay informed of new control products and techniques as they come into the market, but to review the older procedures implemented throughout the company. In short, to continuously improve the process.

Through continued review and upgrading of ESD control equipment and procedures, costs can be maintained at reasonable levels. The corporation will remain free to concentrate on improving productivity, reducing yield losses, and maintaining the reliability of their products. A commitment to the ongoing improvement of ESD control facilities will also make it easier to protect newer, more sensitive devices when they become a part of the operation.

Points To Remember

The key steps to the efficient design and successful implementation of a custom-tailored ESD control program depend on nothing less than a companywide commitment. The individual steps for setting up or strengthening an ESD control program are listed below.

Step 1	Study and understand the technology of ESD control.
Step 2	Gather scientific evidence of the economic value of ESD control.
Step 3	Establish an active ESD committee.
Step 4	Develop a general plan of implementation.
Step 5	Write or adopt a set of realistic handling requirements.
Step 6	Prepare a detailed statement of policy, including individual responsibilities.
Step 7	Prepare a presentation for management.
Step 8	Establish a top management commitment.
Step 9	Develop the details of ESD program management.
Step 10	Present the program to middle and lower management.
Step 11	Begin implementation of the control facilities.
Step 12	Begin training of the entire work force, including management.
Step 13	Begin using facilities immediately after training.
Step 14	Begin formal auditing of all manufacturing departments.
Step 15	Report auditing results, graphically and with regularity, to all levels of management.
Step 16	Continuously improve the process.

Appendix C

An Economic Analysis*

It has now been established that ESD can damage virtually any semiconductor. However, establishing how often that occurs in a specific manufacturing facility, or the consequence of that damage, has proven to be extremely difficult. For that reason, approvals to expend funds for ESD precautions are sought reluctantly and are often denied. This chapter will illustrate a technique that has proven successful in estimating the economic benefit of ESD precautions and, subsequently, in establishing a systematic and cost-effective prevention plan.

Essentially, this approach consists of conducting carefully controlled experiments in a manufacturing environment so as to provide comparisons with and without ESD precautions on given production lines. The results of these experiments will make it possible to justify the general use of ESD precautions on the same production lines, thereby establishing the opportunity to evaluate the impact of ESD precautions on manufacturing. Manufacturing data is then gathered and compared with the experimental data. This combination of experimental and manufacturing data should provide a strong argument for the application of ESD precautions throughout all manufacturing facilities.

For companies starting their own ESD program, the five case studies presented here will provide a solid base of irrefutable economic evidence on which to build a business case. These studies also provide convenient examples for the development of additional experiments on other production lines. *This experimental technique provides a scientific means of not only assessing the impact of ESD damage but also of evaluating which control techniques will be effective and which will be overkill.*

Additional experimental data and case studies may be found in much of the published ESD literature, especially in the proceedings of the EOS/ESD Symposia. The additional data and case studies combined with the experimental data

---

* This Appendix has been reprinted with permission from G.T. Dangelmayer, ESD Program Management, Chapman and Hall, NY, 1990.

presented here, or the results of any proprietary experiments, make a strong case with which to enlist broad based management support for a corporate commitment to ESD control. As ESD control programs are implemented in different manufacturing facilities, the information provided by these experiments can be used to form the basis for realistic handling requirements and for auditing programs that verify across-the-board compliance.

The five case studies are divided, by product line, into three main topics. Case Study 1 (Resistor Failure) briefly documents an isolated experiment involving PWB assembly. Case Studies 2, 3 and 4 focus on the manufacture of components and PWB assemblies and combine experimental data with actual manufacturing data. Case Study 5 demonstrates the difficulty in developing satisfactory control techniques for handling ultrasensitive devices.

Case Study 1: Resistor Failure Due to Automation in Production

Internal customer complaints from an AT&T manufacturing location in North Carolina prompted a study of damaged resistors. The resistors involved were thin film integrated circuit precision resistors, specified to be within a tolerance of +0.2 percent. However, rather than being precise well-controlled resistors, they demonstrated values actually four to five times higher than the intended value. Customer complaints were certainly justified and worthy of close inspection.

The damaged resistors are illustrated in Figure C.1. The resistor on the right shows lightning-like damage appearing as lines running across the material in the pattern of a "crow's foot." The dark area in the photograph is the tantalum nitride that makes up the resistor material. The solid light lines in the tantalum nitride are created by a laser. The laser is used to trim the resistor to a predetermined value with a tolerance of 0.2 percent. The resistor on the left demonstrates clean laser-generated lines and measures 300 ohms. The resistor on the right, with obvious damage sites, measures 1411 ohms.

In searching for the cause of this damage, ESD was identified as one possible cause. To prove the hypothesis, the damage was duplicated with an ESD transient of 450 volts, using the charged-device model. This relatively low threshold of damage to resistors raises many questions, including that of the effect of ESD on silicon devices. A study was initiated to calculate the magnitude of the resistor problem on the manufacturing floor.

Experiment 1

On-site, the average dropout rate for resistors was 20 percent, but some shipments had up to 80 percent losses. In order to determine where the resistors were being damaged, they were tested at each stage of the production line. No failures

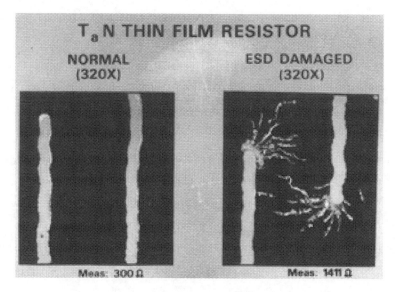

Figure C.1. ESD damaged thin film resistor—"Crows Foot"

were detected until the mass soldering machine. In fact all devices were proven to be in perfect working order prior to their immersion in the mass soldering machine. Boards were then tested at several different points throughout the mass soldering operation.

The mass soldering machine consists of a fluxing station, a soldering station, and a cleaning station. Resistors were tested before and after each of these operations. The damage was determined to be occurring during the cleaning operation.

The cleaning operation was accomplished by nine rotating nylon brushes in a solvent bath. The solvent was highly resistive (1,000,000 megohm-cm) and was actually instrumental in allowing the battery of brushes to charge the boards as they passed through the station. The boards then discharged into the ground of the soldering machine. In the dark, even a casual observer could actually see arcing taking place. There was, in reality, a small lightning storm taking place inside the soldering machine as the boards passed through. As measured by an electrostatic locator, there were charges of up to 6000 volts on some of the boards. (See Figure C.2.)

Using the standard test for defect levels at the conclusion of the manufacturing process, the tester determined that the dropout level of the boards was only 10 percent. That was a surprisingly low incidence of failure in light of the fact that every single PWB assembly was abused with at least nine discharges. It may be taken as an indication of the random behavior of static electricity. However, through tests designed to find resistance shifts that were not caught by the standard test methods, additional failures (amounting to a total of 20 percent) were identified.

	North Carolina	Merrimack Valley
No. of Circuits	100	100
Failures detected after	Mass soldering	Mass soldering
Percent of Defects	20	1
Static Measurements	6000V	1500V
Visible Arching	yes	no
Cleaning solvent	10^{12} Ω- cm	10^{11} Ω - cm
No. of Brushes	9	3

Figure C.2. Two experiments indict PWB cleaning as the source of ESD damage to resistors in 1978.

The remedy to the problem was found in the choice of the cleaning solvent used in the machine. A more conductive solution was necessary (less than 10,000 megohm-cm) to allow the charge to bleed off as quickly as it was created, without the violent discharges taking place. The soldering facility has since been converted to use an aqueous cleaning solution that virtually eliminates the charging.

Experiment 2

Based on the experience with mass soldering machines gained in Experiment 1, a study of the manufacturing facility in North Andover was undertaken. This study was instigated by the discovery of resistor damage on another device (Figure C.3), but this time at the AT&T Merrimack Valley facility in North Andover, Massachusetts. Again, measurements were taken at each stage of the manufacturing process, with particular attention given to the mass soldering operation. The dam-

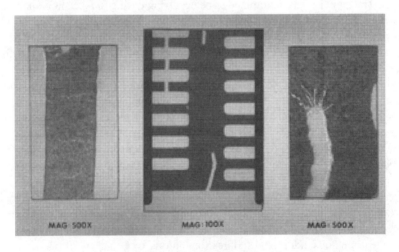

Figure C.3. ESD damaged thin film resistor—"Crows Foot"

age is less severe than that seen at the North Carolina facility, as the charging level was 1500 volts versus 6000 volts (Figure C.2).

As in the earlier experiments, no damage was observed prior to the resistors passing through the mass soldering machine. Within that operation, it was observed that damage occurred during the time that resistors passed through the cleaning station. However, unlike the North Carolina plant, where dropout rates as high as 80 percent were found, a failure rate of only 1 percent was found. Also, the resistance shift out of tolerance was less, only 118 ohms from the specified value of 406 ohms to 624 ohms.

There are two differences between the cleaning machines at North Carolina and Merrimack Valley. First, where the machines in the southern plant had nine brushes, those in the north had three. Second, where the cleaning solvent in North Carolina was highly resistive, the cleaning solvent in the Massachusetts plant was more conductive (100,000 megohm-cm), but not sufficiently conductive to prevent charging.

Consequently, the static potential was measured at approximately 1500 volts instead of 6000 volts. Accordingly, a much lower failure rate was noted among the resistors. Furthermore, additional measurements of resistance produced no evidence of additional failures, as had been the case with the earlier testing. The soldering facility has since been converted to use an aqueous cleaning solution that virtually eliminates the charging.

Case Study 2: Bipolar Discrete Device Failure

The experiments discussed in both this and the following case study were accomplished by randomly selecting samples of the product, splitting these samples into two equal populations, implementing the desired ESD precautions on only one population, and, finally, processing them simultaneously through the manufacturing process. Therefore, the only variables in the experiment were the ESD precautions, thus allowing a scientific look at the impact of these techniques.

Experimental Evidence

Case Study 2 presents an isolated experiment, selected to illustrate that *even older product lines using bipolar devices can benefit* from using wrist straps during manufacturing. The experiment was conducted in 1979 on a PWB assembly line, using as a test vehicle a PWB assembly that had been initially introduced in 1973. This PWB assembly consisted of discrete bipolar transistors as well as integrated circuits. The only form of ESD protection was the introduction of wrist straps to one of the two populations. The sample size for each cell was 216 PWB assemblies; the relative humidity averaged 20 percent.

	ESD Protected (Note)	Unprotected
Final Test Defects	2.3%	6.2%
Relative Humidity	20.0%	20.0%

(Lot Size = 216 PWB assemblies)

Note: Protection consisted of wrist straps only.

Figure C.4. Results of PWB assembly experiment conducted in 1979 on a product initially introduced in 1973

The test results showed significant differences in the two populations, with the unprotected population having 2.7 times the number of test defects than the protected population (see Figure C.4). The defective components were misplaced before a failure mode analysis could be conducted.

In conclusion, the significant improvement (2.3 percent failure versus 6.2 percent) in test defect rates strongly suggests that using wrist straps was beneficial in the manufacture of this older bipolar product. However, without the diagnostics, a final conclusion was difficult to arrive at. Therefore, another experiment was conducted using a different product.

Case Study 3: Device and PWB Assembly Failures

This case study represents a particularly complete collection of both experimental and manufacturing data. It is a study of the ESD behavior of a bipolar Hybrid Integrated Circuit (HIC) during manufacture, as well as during PWB assembly and test.

The following studies were initiated as a result of external customer complaints from telephone companies and unusually high failure rates. It was determined that *PWB assemblies were failing on customer premises due to ESD damage.* A bipolar junction on HIC "A" on the PWB assembly was exhibiting excessive leakage, resulting in system disruption. The junction damage encountered is shown in Figure C.5 in a photograph of a field failure.

The ESD-induced failure reveals nearly identical damage to that resulting from ESD testing using the HBM.[34,35] The threshold of damage was established to be 700 volts.

Experiments were conducted in the HIC manufacturing shop and in a PWB assembly shop. After ESD precautions were introduced, additional data was drawn from the two shops. While manufacturing data by itself may be highly suspect due to the large number of variables involved in the manufacturing process, definitive conclusions can certainly be drawn when manufacturing evidence is supported by experimental data.

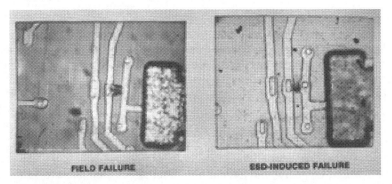

Figure C.5. Comparison of a field failure (1000x) and an ESD-induced failure (1000x) of a bipolar junction

Experiment 1

This experiment was conducted in the HIC manufacturing shop where the relative humidity is regulated between 30 and 50 percent year-round. The selected test vehicle was HIC "A," described above. The ESD precautions, unique to the protected population, consisted of wrist straps and static dissipative tote trays. The sample size was 1275 HICs in each group.

As part of the manufacturing process, both populations were tested twice: once at an in-process test station and again at final test. The results were nearly the same at both test operations, with the unprotected HICs yielding significantly more defects than the protected population (Figure C.6). During the in-process testing, the unprotected population had a defect rate of 4.5 percent, compared to 2.4 percent for the protected population, or 1.9 times the number of electrical defects. In the final test, the unprotected population had a defect rate of 2.9 percent versus 1.2 percent for the protected HICs, or 2.4 times as many defects.

All defects were analyzed specifically for evidence of ESD damage, and none were found in the protected population. However, approximately half of the defects in the unprotected group were ESD induced, totally accounting for the difference in the two populations.

In conclusion, the difference in the defect rates between the two populations was found to be statistically *significant with a confidence level of 99.9 percent.* Additionally, failure mode analysis confirmed that the difference was due to ESD damage. Therefore, by virtue of the design of the experiment, it can be assumed with the same level of confidence that the introduction of wrist straps and static dissipative tote trays was effective in the prevention of ESD damage to the protected population. Neither conductive nor shielding materials were used at any point during this experiment.

Experiment 2

Because the results had been so definitive in the HIC shop, it was decided to extend the experiment into the PWB assembly shop and to design the experiment to determine whether the ESD precautions taken in the HIC shop had influenced the quality of the outgoing HICs. This was accomplished by marking all of the good HICs in Experiment 1 such that the parent population could be determined later. The HICs were then transported between the two manufacturing shops with the protected HICs in the new conductive foam and the unprotected HICs in the old expanded polystyrene (EPS) shipping trays. The use of EPS trays was formerly standard procedure but has since been replaced by conductive foam. The HICs were mixed and randomly introduced into the PWB assembly manufacturing process and allowed to proceed without supervision, with one exception. Employees at test positions were instructed to pull out any defects with the unique markings.

It is important to note that, at this time, the PWB assembly shop was not employing any form of ESD protection.

The results revealed that the defect rate of the HICs that had been unprotected in the HIC shops was 5.5 times greater than the defect rate of those that had been protected. Several HICs were damaged during removal from the PWB assemblies, and therefore, failure mode analysis was not possible. Figure C.6 summarizes the results for both Experiment 1 and Experiment 2.

In conclusion, the difference in defect ratio of 5.5 to 1 was found to be *statistically significant with a confidence level of 90 percent.*

Therefore, in addition to reducing defect rates by approximately 2 to 1, the ESD precautions taken earlier probably enhanced the quality of the outgoing HICs as well. This supports the fact that ESD damage can be cumulative and latent.

	ESD Protected	Unprotected	Ratio
HIC shop:			
First Test Defects	2.4%	4.5%	1.9
Final Test Defects	1.2%	2.9%	2.4
Relative Humidity	35.0%	35.0%	
Continuation—EQ Shop (Without Protection)			
Defect Rates	0.4%	2.2%	5.5

(Lot Size = 1275 HICs, each group)

Figure C.6. Results for HIC Experiments 1 and 2

PWB Assembly Shop—Failure Analysis

As a separate investigation to further understand HIC "A," 302 defective HICs were randomly selected from the PWB assembly shops for FMA purposes. The results, as shown in Figure C.7, revealed that 39 percent of the defects were ESD-induced with characteristics nearly identical to Figure C.5.

Additionally, it is possible that a portion of the 48 percent with no trouble found had at one time intermittent defects due to ESD. This is because the device in question has a tendency to latch with subthreshold ESD events and then recover when removed from bias.

In conclusion, it was determined experimentally that ESD precautions taken in the manufacture of HIC "A" resulted in a 2 to 1 improvement at both test operations and, at the same time, substantially improved the outgoing quality. Additionally, a major portion (39 percent) of the defects created during PWB assembly manufacture were ESD induced. If these observations are valid, the general application of ESD precautions would generate manufacturing data to substantiate them. This assumption was confirmed with a financial analysis of the manufacturing process as described in the subsections that follow.

Manufacturing Evidence

Comparisons are made in the following subsections between the earlier experimental data and manufacturing data gathered subsequent to the systematic introduction of ESD precautions throughout the shops. The actual precautions taken in each area will be defined. In addition, in 1981, HIC "A" was redesigned to provide better ESD immunity, recoded, and phased-in over a 5-month period. The ESD threshold of this HIC was improved from 700 to 2100 volts.

Manufacturing evidence by itself can only be considered as strong circumstantial evidence. This is because operations of these types are governed by countless variables. However, in conjunction with experimental data, definitive conclusions may properly be made.

No trouble found	48%
ESD-induced defects	39%
Miscellaneous defects	13%

(Sample Size: 302 HICs)

Figure C.7. PWB assembly shop failure mode analysis results

HIC Shop Manufacturing Data

Two accounting methods, cost reduction and nonconformance cost, were selected to illustrate the economic benefits experienced subsequent to the introduction of the general use of ESD precautions for all products in the HIC shop. They are each discussed in the following paragraphs.

The first accounting method, cost reduction, is a formal process that requires certification from the accounting organization to validate the calculations and data documentation. In this instance and for all product lines in the HIC shop, a three-month average yield was recorded prior to incorporating ESD precautions. The general use of wrist straps and static dissipative tote trays was then introduced during a three-month grace period. Following this, another set of three-month average yields was established for comparison purposes.

The composite results are shown in Figure C.8, where the actual yield improvements were 1.3 and 3.3 times better than experimentally predicted (Experiment 2) for the in-process and final tests, respectively.

The discrepancy is not particularly surprising since only one of the many products in production was discussed in Experiment 2. This data represents all products in production at the time, and it therefore follows that HIC "A" was not a worst-case situation. In addition, the rate of *return on investment was 950 percent*; therefore, the prevention techniques used were extremely cost-effective.

The second accounting method, nonconformance cost, is maintained as an independent measurement of manufacturing performance. It is an indicator of both the material and labor financial losses associated with a discarded product. It logically follows that the significant yield improvements described above must translate into major reductions in the nonconformance costs.

Figure C.9 is a graph of the nonconformance cost performance of the HIC shop during and after the introduction of ESD precautions. It is a plot of the ratio of actual expense dollars to forecasted expense dollars versus time ($/$ versus time). Without specifying the details of the operation, the manufacturing conditions were such that the forecasted expense dollars may be considered essentially constant for the 3-year period shown.

Therefore, the changes in the graph correlate directly to changes in actual expense dollars incurred due to a nonconforming product. Clearly, there is a

	Experimental	Actual	Ratio
First test	2.4%	3%	1.3
Final test	1.2%	6%	3.3

Rate of return on investment—950%

Figure C.8. A comparison of actual HIC shop cost reduction results to experimental defect levels show reasonable correlation

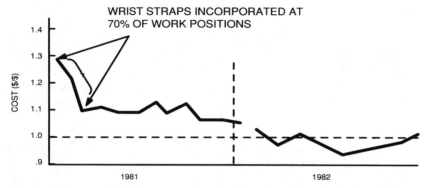

Figure C.9. HIC shop nonconformance cost ($/$) (actual $/forecasted $)

marked improvement during the course of 1981. In fact, a 20 percent reduction is noted when comparing the first quarter of 1981 to that of 1982.

The introduction of ESD precautions began in October 1980. By the end of the first quarter of 1981, approximately 70 percent of the work positions were equipped with wrist straps. *The introduction of wrist straps coincides with the sharp decrease in nonconformance cost.*

Additional precautions were phased-in during the balance of the year, which contributed to the continuing downward trend of the graph. These additions included the remaining wrist strap installations, dissipative tote trays and employee training.

In conclusion, the two independent accounting methods presented established strong circumstantial evidence that ESD precautions were extremely cost-effective when applied to the entire HIC shop manufacturing process and that the improvements were consistent with the experimental predictions for HICs. This does not address the impact on PWB assemblies; therefore, the investigation was further extended.

PWB Assembly Shop Manufacturing Data

In February 1982, the PWB assembly manufacturing shop was fully equipped with wrist straps, heelstraps, dissipative table mats, and floor mats, where appropriate. A high degree of employee compliance with ESD procedures was achieved almost immediately as a result of the experience gained in the HIC shop. The impact of these precautions on HIC "A" can be estimated from the experimental data.

Experimentally, it was concluded that at least 39 percent of the HIC "A" defects found in the PWB assembly shop were ESD induced and that precautions taken in the HIC shop had improved the outgoing HIC quality. However, the experimental data had not yet been substantiated with manufacturing results.

The PWB assembly manufacturing results obtained subsequent to the introduction of ESD precautions augmented the experimental results and were documented in four different ways. The first observation was an abrupt reduction of 60
percent in the defect rate of HICs. Next, there was a sharp reduction in the nonconformance cost. Then, a formal cost-reduction investigation established a cost-
effective rate of *return on Investment of 185 percent*. The fourth measure of
improvement confirmed the enhancement of outgoing quality in a report by the
Quality Assurance (QA) Department.

The Quality Assurance Department statistically samples and tests outgoing
PWB assemblies for compliance with system requirements during a 24-hour
system test. Defects are then analyzed and reports generated for analysis and
corrective action, if necessary. One such report separates failures attributable
to HICs and is graphically represented in Figure C.10 for 1980, 1981, and
1982.

HIC failures are plotted as a percentage of the total HICs sampled on PWB
assemblies versus time. Two marked improvements (2.1 and 1.6 to 1) are noted,
which coincide with the introduction of ESD precautions first in the HIC shop in
late 1980 and, later, in the PWB assembly shop in early 1982. These improvements are consistent with the results of Experiment 2, where outgoing HIC quality was enhanced by 5.5 to 1.

If these observations are valid, the field performance of PWB assemblies produced in 1982 would be better than those produced prior to 1981. This assumption
was confirmed by reviewing field return data on a representative sample of PWB

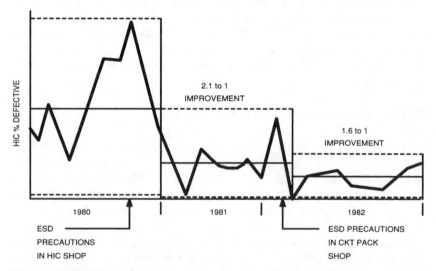

**Figure C.10. Quality assurance sampling of outgoing PWB assemblies–percent defec-
tive HICs versus time**

assembly codes at comparable points in the product maturity cycle. The failure-in-time (FIT) rates of 1982-vintage PWB assemblies were found to be significantly better than those manufactured prior to 1981.

A composite reduction in QA defect rates of approximately 3 to 1 occurred on two separate occasions, coinciding with the introduction of ESD precautions. Also, a significant improvement in field performance was consistent with the improvements in the outgoing PWB assembly quality reflected in the QA data. At the same time, yield, cost reduction, and nonconformance cost indicators showed marked improvements.

In conclusion, it was predicted, and proven through experiments, that ESD precautions would significantly improve yields in both areas of manufacture, as well as enhance the outgoing HIC quality. Coincident with the introduction of ESD precautions and an ESD redesign, *four separate measures of manufacturing performance confirmed that the improvements did occur.*

This combination of experimental and manufacturing evidence, in conjunction with the timing, can lead to only one conclusion. ESD precautions, both in design and handling, are not only cost-effective but are also necessary to achieve the highest levels of outgoing quality and reliability. This conclusion applies to both component and PWB assembly manufacture. However, it is recognized that ESD control is not the only contributing factor here. For instance, during the same 3-year period, design, test, and manufacturing improvements were also incorporated. One of the design changes was the HIC "A" redesign which provided better ESD immunity.

Case Study 4: Latent Failure Due to Prior ESD Damage

This case history was selected to illustrate a latent failure due to prior ESD damage in a HIC design using a bipolar silicon integrated circuit.

Experimental Evidence

The first evidence of a problem appeared in the early stages of initial production during a quality assurance sampling when 3 out of 15 PWB assemblies failed the system test. These PWB assemblies had just passed an identical system test as part of the manufacturing process, which did not include ESD protection. Subsequent defect analysis revealed a bipolar junction on HIC "B" with excessive leakage in all three PWB assemblies. Also, the failing external HIC pin was routed directly to another HIC on the PWB and not to an external PWB assembly connector pin.

Later, an unrelated laboratory evaluation of 24 of the same type of PWB assemblies was initiated. The PWB assemblies were put into an operating system,

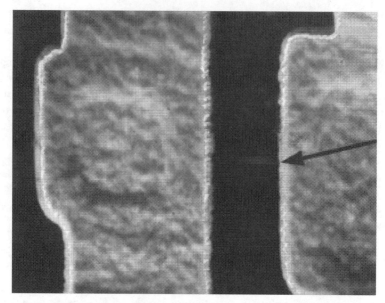

Figure C.11. Latent ESD failure—bipolar junction

tested successfully, and then left functioning in a secured area. During the next 5 days, 5 of the 24 PWB assemblies failed with the leakage condition described above. Figure C.11 is a scanning electronic microscope (SEM) photograph (at 4800X) of the junction damage exhibited by all five failures.

Although it is difficult to see, there is a faint trace between the two conductors, indicated by the arrow. The damage was subsequently duplicated by exposure to ESD. The threshold of damage was established at 450 volts HBM for HIC "B" and at 1000 volts HBM for the completed PWB assembly.

The circumstances surrounding these five failures were such that no one could have touched them once they were operating in the system. Additionally, the testing was done by remote access. Therefore, it is likely that these failures were latent due to prior ESD damage.

At approximately the same time, one customer reported that 17 PWB assemblies out of 31 failed two weeks after being successfully put into service. All exhibited the same leakage condition as the five laboratory failures and were suspected of having latent ESD failures.

In comparing this failure activity to the in-house data above, a statistically significant difference is noted with a confidence level of 99 percent. Likewise, a review of the field data indicated that this situation was extremely abnormal. Therefore, unique and severe conditions triggered the 17 failures. Further evaluation revealed that these PWB assemblies had been expedited through unusual channels in the dry winter months and that they had been transported in EPS trays.

Furthermore, these PWB assemblies were daughter boards and required assembly to the mother board on customer premises. During assembly, it is particularly convenient and almost necessary for the installer to directly contact the conductor on the PWB leading to the indicated HIC pin, thereby increasing the probability of ESD damage. Therefore, most likely the EPS packaging, in conjunction with the circumstances in the field, was probably a major factor leading to latent failure. However, prior damage in the factory or in transit could not be ruled out.

Compared to the number of failures during early production, these failures were insignificant and were the only ones reported. However, on the premise that it was an early warning, response was prompt—ESD precautions were incorporated throughout the manufacturing and shipping process and a Zener diode was added to the PWB assembly to shunt ESD transients to ground. Adding the diode improved the PWD assembly threshold from 1000 volts to something in excess of 15,000 volts. As a longer-term solution, HIC "B" was redesigned to incorporate additional protection.

In conclusion, latent failure due to prior ESD damage was witnessed under laboratory conditions and was suspected of having occurred on customer premises while the PWB assemblies were in service as a result of EPS packaging. This, in conjunction with other reports of latency,[36] supports previous conclusions that ESD damage can adversely affect the reliability of bipolar devices.

Case Study 5: Ultrasensitive Devices

The trend toward including ultrasensitive devices in the manufacturing process calls for a separate discussion of the problems and difficulties that can arise in handling these devices. One such case was revealed with the introduction of an N-type metal oxide semiconductor (NMOS) device that had an *ESD threshold of 20 volts*. Major problems were encountered during device fabrication as well as during the assembly of PWB assemblies.

Device Testing

Since production levels of this particular NMOS device were still quite low, each device was precious and expensive. This low level of production was due in part to difficulties experienced during the fabrication and testing of this extremely sensitive device. Yields at the device plant were vacillating widely. For instance, during one test operation, an exceptionally high dropout rate was noted. As many as 40 to 60 percent of the devices coming though the line were lost.

It was recognized that the test fixture was made of TEFLON * material and highly prone to charging. Also, only one of several employees was experiencing this high dropout rate.

The employee experiencing the high dropout rate had exceptionally long fingernails. Other employees with shorter nails were not experiencing the high failure rates because they inadvertently touched most of the leads, creating a shunt and grounding the device. Thus, when the device was brought into the field created by the TEFLON material, charge separation was not taking place and the device was not being damaged. On the other hand, the employee who held each device with long fingernails was not grounding the devices on which she worked. Consequently, as these devices were brought into the field, charge separation was taking place. As the test set engaged the device's conductors, discharge occurred causing damage and a high failure rate.

Two solutions presented themselves. The first was to exclusively use employees with short fingernails. The second and more effective, was to redesign the test fixture in question in order to eliminate the TEFLON material and thus the static field. In this way, charge separation could not take place regardless of fingernail length nor could the devices be damaged. Conventional ESD control techniques such as wrist straps did not solve this problem.

PWB Assembly

Extreme fluctuations in PWB assembly yields (Figure C.12) were occurring during the start of "ramp up," that period during which production quantity begins to increase rapidly in order to meet the ultimate levels of production. Between the months of June and September of 1987, the removal rate varied dramatically between 10 and 30 percent. In actual lot-to-lot observation, *some lots showed a 100 percent dropout* in which every single device was defective.

Due to the scarcity of these 20-volt NMOS devices, the cost implications of their continued failure were very high. Therefore, a detailed investigation was undertaken. Through failure analysis, it was determined that the devices were failing due to ESD. In fact, it was demonstrated through failure mode analysis at Bell Laboratories, that virtually all of the failures were ESD induced. However, no solution for handling a device that failed at 20 volts was readily apparent.

A special detailed audit was conducted, and a number of people experienced in different aspects of the issue were consulted. A detailed inspection of the manufacturing line was begun, and an action plan of things needing to be corrected was compiled. Based on that action plan, a task force was assembled and assigned to correct deficiencies in the line and to report weekly on what corrective measures

* Registered Trademark of E. I. Du Pont De Nemours & Co., Inc.

had been taken. Because of the extreme seriousness of this situation, the weekly reports were channeled to high-level executives in the company.

Initially, all kinds of extraordinary handling precautions were instituted. Yet, even with all of this special attention and with the fullest compliance with the procedures defined by Class I rating (Chapter 7, "Realistic Requirements"), yields continued to fluctuate dramatically from June through September (Figure C.12).

The solution to this particular problem was found in the introduction of a "top hat." A top hat is a conductive shunt that is placed on top of a device after it has been assembled to the PWB. As soon as these problem-causing ultrasensitive devices arrived at the assembling operation and immediately after they were assembled to the PWB assembly, the shunt, electrically shorting the leads together, was placed on top. The board was then allowed to go through the production line in normal sequence. The results of the inauguration of that procedure during the month of September are clearly and dramatically recorded in Figure C.12. By mid-November the removal rate had dropped even further to around 2 percent. In short, by the simple addition of a shunt to the devices, a dropout rate of 30 percent was reduced to 2 percent.

The simplicity of this solution is particularly striking in contrast to more common procedures involving every kind of ESD protective device known to science. The use of so many kinds of precautions eventually becomes difficult to manage. In cases such as this, when an ultrasensitive device is so easily damaged, the extraordinary measure of using a multitude of standard precautions may prove futile as

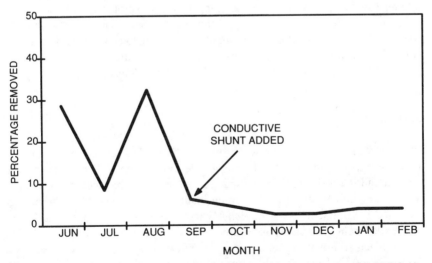

Figure C.12. PWB assembly yield variation due to ESD damage of an NMOS device with a 20-volt threshold

well as expensive. The solution described here introduces a simple shunt into a Class I set of procedures. The incremental cost is trivial. A total expenditure of $1000 provided the level of protection required. Yet the dollar savings realized on the production line excluding overhead expenses, reached $6.2 million per year for this one device on this one line. That is an impressive payback by any measure.

One additional benefit derived from this case was the impact that it had on the design community. Asked to justify a threshold of 20 volts for the NMOS device involved in the project, designers responded by redesigning the device and raising the level of sensitivity to 1000 volts HBM, a remarkable accomplishment.

In conclusion, this case study makes it clear that ultrasensitive devices can present a potential threat to production lines that may result in lost production and lost sales. The financial implications are particularly unattractive when the cost of lost sales is added to the cost of lost materials. Note that the PWB assembly, in its final configuration, is enclosed in a metal housing. Consequently, this ultrasensitive device has always been well protected in the field and has a low return level for ESD defects.

As a direct result of the experience outlined in this case study, minimum design requirements were modified and a new set of handling requirements (Class 0)[11] were established and added to the AT&T handbook, as detailed in Chapter 7, "Realistic Requirements." It was apparent that *a cookbook approach to establishing handling criteria for ultrasensitive devices would not work*. For example, it is likely that some of the automated equipment used in the assembly process was causing the problem solved by the application of a top hat. Clearly, all of the wrist straps and ionization units in the world would not have solved this problem. Adding a shunt was not only necessary but sufficient to protect the device at great economic benefit. The solution offered tremendous economic leverage. In addition, a Class 1 shop was allowed, through this solution, to continue to do business as usual while protecting an ultrasensitive device. Training considerations were minimized, and the impact on personnel significantly simplified.

Conclusion

The experimental approach presented in this chapter has proven to be an effective tool to assess, in advance, the benefits of introducing ESD precautions into a manufacturing process. The experiments, with a reasonable degree of accuracy, predicted significant yield and outgoing quality improvement for both components and PWB assemblies. The design, execution, and failure mode analysis of such experiments ultimately determine whether or not a definitive conclusion can be reached. For instance, selecting an ESD-sensitive test vehicle increases the likelihood of detecting a difference between two populations. These experiments, although time consuming, are relatively inexpensive to run and provide ample justification for equipping a product line and ultimately a factory with ESD precautions.

However, it is the combination of experimental and manufacturing data that provides compelling justification for providing ESD protection systematically throughout manufacturing facilities. The evidence, as presented, establishes that ESD precautions are cost-effective for the protection of even older bipolar designs and contribute substantially to overall improvements in outgoing product quality and reliability. It can also be assumed that as trends in technology continue to produce devices of ever-increasing susceptibility to ESD, the economic benefits of incorporating ESD precautions will increase accordingly.

Therefore, based on the cases presented here, it is recommended that a systematic ESD prevention plan that extends from design through customer acceptance be implemented. The design effort is logically directed at the more sensitive devices, while handling precautions are judiciously applied to all solid-state devices such that the more susceptible are provided increased ESD protection.

For facilities faced with having to justify implementation of a new program of ESD controls, the case histories reviewed in this chapter provide irrefutable evidence of the economic benefit to be gained by such a program. Some returns on investment recorded here are as high as 1000 percent. In the example of the NMOS device in Case Study 5, *an investment of only $1000 resulted in a savings of $6 million.* While this is an isolated incident, it is patently clear that an outstanding level of return can be expected from any judicious investment in ESD precautions.

ESD precautions produce yield improvement across the board. All product lines gain from ESD control, although the extent of that improvement will vary among product lines. With the introduction of an ESD program, it is reasonable to expect an average yield improvement of approximately 5 percent, as well as reliability and quality improvements of the outgoing product.

It is also likely that certain catastrophic situations will occur, resulting in very poor yields that could approach zero, such as that described in the NMOS case history. At times, variations in yield can appear so extreme as to suggest multiple causes and to require prompt action. The ideal resolution is to solve such problems on the spot. For that, a local expert is required. There is a need for someone close by who can solve problems of that complexity in a timely, economically sound manner.

It is even more important to be able to prevent damaging situations. The design of an ESD control plan should take into account the probability of such occurrences so that they can be systematically anticipated and prevented. The resulting improvement in yields can be every bit as dramatic as some of those illustrated here.

In many cases designers hold the key to ESD success. They must understand ESD phenomenon and its impact and how to design-in the highest level of protection from ESD damage. See Chapter 5 "Designed-in Protection and Product Testing" for more details.

Points To Remember

- The type of scientific analysis presented in this chapter provides a solid basis for realistic control measures.
- The combination of experimental and manufacturing data provides compelling justification for ESD control measures.
- A strong management commitment to a corporate ESD control program can be enlisted by using the data provided in this chapter or by conducting similar experiments to establish the economic significance of ESD control.
- A review of papers presented at EOS/ESD symposia will yield additional convincing evidence of the economic benefits of ESD control.
- ESD controls can lower operating costs with a rate of return on investment of up to 1000 percent and enhance outgoing quality and reliability.
- Two independent accounting methods confirmed that ESD precautions were extremely cost-effective in the manufacture of HICs.
- Quality assurance sampling of outgoing PWB assemblies revealed a 3 to 1 improvement in defect levels, which coincided with the introduction of ESD controls in the manufacturing process.
- As technology trends continue to produce devices of ever-increasing susceptibility to ESD, the economic benefits of incorporating ESD precautions will increase accordingly.
- ESD precautions, both in design and handling, are not only cost effective but are also necessary to achieve the highest levels of outgoing quality and reliability.
- To avoid excessive implementation costs, ultrasensitive devices require extraordinary measures that must be carefully tailored to the specific situation.

GLOSSARY

air ion

An air ion (or atmospheric ion) is a molecular cluster of 10–15 molecules (mostly water) around an oxygen (negative ion) or nitrogen molecule (negative or positive) that has gained or lost an electron. An ion is characterized by its mobility. The **mobility** of a negative air ion is about $1.8 \cdot 10^{-4}\,\mathrm{m^2 V^{-1} s^{-1}}$ and of a positive ion about $1.4 \cdot 10^{-4}\,\mathrm{m^2 V^{-1} s^{-1}}$. *See also* **ionization**.

ampere, A

Fundamental unit (in SI, international system of units) for electric current, defined by the forces between parallel wires carrying DC currents.

antistatic agent

Substance to be applied to insulative material to make it sufficiently conductive. Surface-active antistatic agents (e.g. quaternary ammonium halogenides) form a thin layer on the surface; this layer will attract moisture from the surrounding air. Bulk-active agents (often amines or amides) are compounded with a polymere and will diffuse to the surface, where it attracts moisture (pink poly). In some materials (e.g. rubber and many plastics), conductivity may be increased substantially by the addition of carbon black.

antistatic material

Old designation for material with surface resistivity $\rho_s < 10^{10}\,\Omega$. Often used colloquially for materials that do not retain static charges.

astatic material

Old designation for material with a surface resistivity $\rho_s = 10^{10} - 10^{14}\,\Omega$.

breakdown, electrical

If the field strength exceeds the **breakdown field strength** along some path from a charged conductor to ground (or to a conductor at a different potential), ions are formed along the whole path, resulting in an electrical breakdown.

breakdown field strength, (dielectric strength)

Field strength at which incidental electrons in a dielectric, for instance air, receives sufficient energy over their mean free path to cause ionization by collision. Breakdown field strength (between plane electrodes): Air $=$ $3 \cdot 10^6$ V $\cdot$ m^{-1}; plexiglass $= 4 \cdot 10^7$ V $\cdot$ m^{-1}.

breakdown voltage

Minimum voltage between insulated conductor and ground where **breakdown field strength** is exceeded along some path.

brush discharge

Electrical discharge between electrode of small radius of curvature (a few millimeters) and ground along irregular, luminescent paths. Low energy density. May ignite certain vapor mixtures.

capacitance

An insulated conductor has a capacitance C with respect to ground if a charge q raises the conductor to a voltage V related by $q = CV$. Unit for capacitance is farad (F) defined by

$$1 \text{ farad} = 1 \frac{\text{coulomb}}{\text{volt}}$$

The concept capacitance can only be applied to insulated conductors. In an electrostatic context, most capacitances are on the order of 10–1,000 pF, i.e., $10^{11} - 10^{-9}$ F.

capacitor

In a static electric context, any insulated conductor is a capacitor, with a certain **capacitance** with respect to ground.

carbon black

See **antistatic agent.**

charge

Property of certain elementary particles, primarily electrons (negative) and protons (positive). Opposite charges (positive/negative) attract each other like charges (positive/positive and negative/negative) repel each other. Unit for charge is coulomb (C) defined by

$$1 \text{ coulomb} = 1 \text{ ampere} \cdot \text{second}$$

All electrical phenomena are caused by intercharge forces. *See also* **electric field**. A body is negatively charged if it has an excess of electrons, positively charged if it has a deficit of electrons.

charge carriers (mobile)

All materials contain mobile charge carriers, to some extent. In metals, the carriers are electrons in plentitude; in electrolytes and air, they are ions (although very different in character), and in insulators and semiconductors they are holes (or electron vacancies) in widely varying concentration. *See also* **mobility.**

charge decay

A charge located on an insulator or insulated conductor will gradually be neutralized by attracting oppositely charged carriers. Except for a negatively charged conductor (where the charge is electrons), a charge may never be literally removed from a charged body. The **decay rate** depends on the **resistivity** of the contacting medium and on the geometry of the setup.

charge density

The concentration of charge on a surface determines the **field strength** in front of the surface. Maximum charge density in atmospheric air at the surface of conductor is about $3 \cdot 10^{-5}\,C \cdot m^2$.

charge plate monitor, CPM

Instrument for comparing efficiency of different ionization systems. A bare metal plate with a capacitance of ~ 15 pF is charged (e.g., to 1000 V), and its voltage is monitored as a function of time by a field meter.

charged device model

See **ESD damage models.**

conductance

See **Ohm's law.**

conductive material

Material with surface resistivity $\rho_s < 10^5\,\Omega$.

conductivity

Reciprocal of **resistivity**. Unit for conductivity is $\Omega^{-1}\,m^{-1}$. See also **resistivity, resistance, surface resistivity, Ohm's law.**

conductor

Body made of material with (bulk) **resistivity** lower than about $10^{-6} - 10^{-7}\,\Omega m$. Most conductors are metals.

contact electrification

Charging of materials primarily by contract, caused by difference in work functions. *See also* **triboelectrification.**

corona discharge

Electrical discharge from conductive electrode (sharp point or thin wire), where the **breakdown field strength** is exceeded in a small region in front of the electrode and where positive and negative ions are formed in equal numbers. Also called silent discharge. Low energy density. A corona discharge cannot ignite any vapor/gas mixture.

coulomb, C

Unit for charge defined by 1 coulomb = 1 ampere · second $(1A \cdot 1s)$. *See also* **charge**.

current, current density

Transport of charge caused by an electric field. Unit for current is **ampere, A**. Current density is current per unit area perpendicular to direction of current, unit $A \cdot m^{-2}$.

D-field

See **dielectric displacement.**

D-flux

See **flux.**

decay rate

Rate of **neutralization** of field from charge on a body. In the case of a capacitive system with the capacitance C and grounding resistance R, the charge will be neutralized exponentially according to the formula

$$q = q_0 e^{-\frac{t}{\tau}}$$

where the **time constant** τ is given by $\tau = RC$. In the case of a material with a (bulk) resistivity ρ and permittivity ε, a charge will be neutralized exponentially with the time constant $\tau = \rho\varepsilon$. τ is the time it takes the charge to decay to $1/e \sim 0.37$. In case of surface charge decay, the decay rate cannot be predicted from material parameters.

decay of charge

See **charge decay.**

dielectric

Material that is being polarized (i.e., **dipoles** being formed) when exposed to an electric field. The name dielectric is normally used only on polarizable insulators. If a field E from a constant charge is being filled by a dielectric, the field strength is reduced by a factor ε_r, **the relative permittivity** or **dielectric constant** characteristic for the dielectric. *See also* **polarization, permittivity.**

dielectric constant

See **dielectric.**

dielectric displacement, electrical field density, D

Quantity characterizing the ability of an electric field to cause **induction**. An induced charge density σ is caused by a dielectric displacement $D = \sigma$. Unit for dielectric displacement $C \cdot m^{-2}$. In isotropic media the dielectric displacement D is related to the electric field E by $D = \varepsilon E$ where ε is the **permittivity** of the medium. *See also* **flux.**

dielectric strength

See **breakdown field strength.**

dipole

An electric dipole is a positive and negative charge of same numerical value at a fixed distance from each other. Dipoles are formed in **dielectrics** when these are exposed to an external field. The field from the dipoles will be superimposed on the external field resulting in a lowered field strength (for a fixed field-creating charge). An airborne particle (dust) in an electric field will be polarized and from a dipole and move in the direction of (numerically) increasing field strength. See **dielectric.**

discharge

See **brush discharge, corona discharge, spark discharge.**

E-field

See **electric field.**

electret

Permanently polarized material, e.g., Teflon (approximate electrical equivalent of permanent magnet).

electric field

Region in which an electric charge experiences a force (from other charges). If the force on a charge q is F the **field strength** E is defined by $F = qE$. Unit for field strength is

$$\frac{\text{newton}}{\text{coulomb}} \quad \text{which is identical to} \quad \frac{\text{volt}}{\text{meter}}, \quad \text{V} \cdot \text{m}^{-1}$$

See also **flux, breakdown field strength**.

E-flux

See **flux**.

electrofilter

Device in which airborne particulates are being charged in a corona discharge and precipitated (plated out) by an electric field.

electrometer

Instrument for measuring voltage (difference) with very low current ($< 10^{-15}$ A) passing through the instrument.

electrostatic energy

If a capacitive system with capacitance C is charged to a voltage V by a charge $q = CV$, the system stores an electrostatic energy.

$$W = \frac{q^2}{2C} = \frac{1}{2} CV^2$$

which may be dissipated in a **spark**, possibly causing ignition of an explosive atmosphere. *See* **ignition energy**.

electrostatics, static electricity

The science of the effects of electric charges located on insulators or insulated conductors. These effects may well include the movement or displacement of charges, for instance, by **induction, polarization, ionization**, and **plateout**. The designation **static electricity** is sometimes used colloquially to mean primarily the harmful or unwanted effects of electrostatic charges.

elementary ion

Nitrogen or oxygen molecule having lost an electron (positive elementary ion) or oxygen molecule having captured an electron (negative elementary ion) before clustering with water molecules to form ordinary **air** (or atmospheric) **ions**.

emitter

Conductive electrode in the form of thin wire or sharp points. If emitter is held at a voltage of a few kilovolt (kV) with respect to surroundings, air ions are formed in a corona discharge in a small region in front of the electrode. If electrode is positive, the positive ions are repelled as if they are emitted from the electrode. However, the emitter **does not** emit ions–it collects ions, in this case, negative ions. The ions are formed by the high field strength in front of the electrode, not by the high voltage.

electrostatic discharge, ESD

Originally simply meaning any discharge caused by an electrostatic charge collection, whether in the chemical, textile, or other industries. Today more or less copyrighted by the electronic industry to mean any kind of electrostatic problem involving semiconductor components or devices.

ESD, *See* **electrostatic discharge.**

ESD, damage models

There are two main circuit models for damaging components or circuits by an electrical discharge: the **human body model**—imitating the effect of the discharge from a charged person, consisting of a capacitor (often 100 pF) with one terminal grounded in series with a resistor of 1000 Ω; and the **machine model**—imitating the discharge from a charged insulated conductor consisting of a capacitor with one terminal grounded. Other important models are the **charged device model** and **field-induced model**.

farad

Unit for **capacitance**

$$1 \text{ farad} = 1 \frac{\text{coulomb}}{\text{volt}}$$

faraday cage, faraday screen

Conductive enclosure that cuts off the (static) field from external charges.

faraday pail

Insulated conductive container to be connected to charge meter. When charged item is placed in pail, the charge may be read on meter.

field

See **electric field.**

field ionization

See **ionization.**

field lines

Mathematical lines to give a qualitative impression of a field. A two-dimensional plot, however, will never give a true picture of a three-dimensional field.

field meter

Instrument for measuring electric fields. A field meter will normally distort the field to be measured and will show a higher field strength than the undisturbed value. The reading of a field meter (determined by the D-field, rather than the E-field) refers to the field strength at the face of the sensor, not at the surface of the charged body.

flux

Surface integral of perpendicular component of a field over a surface S
flux of electric field E

$$\Phi_E = \int_S E \cdot dS$$

If the surface S is a closed surface surrounding a charge q, we have the **Gauss'
law** (or **theorem**) for the E-field.

$$\Phi_E = \int_{\text{closed surface, } S} E \cdot dS = \frac{q}{\varepsilon}$$

where ε is the **permittivity** in the region of the surface S and correspondingly
for the D-field

$$\Phi_D = \int_{\text{closed surface, } S} D \cdot dS = q$$

Gauss' law (or **theorem**)
   See **flux.**

ground
Conductive region (not necessarily the earth) with sufficiently high capacitance
relative to which potentials are measured and to which charges may decay.

hand-held meter
Instrument for locating electric charges by reacting to the electric field (or
rather, the D-field).

human body model
   See **ESD damage models.**

ignition energy
Necessary energy to ignite vapor/gas or dust (powder)/gas mixture. Minimum
ignition energy for mixtures of many organic vapors (e.g., ethly ether, acetone,
cyclopropane) with atmospheric air is about 0.2 mJ, with pure oxygen about 1
μJ. Minimum ignition energy for powder/atmospheric air mixtures about
10–100 times higher.

incendiveness
The ability of an electrical discharge to start an ignition or explosion in a
gas/vapor or dust/vapor mixture. *See* **ignition energy, corona discharge,
brush discharge, spark discharge.**

induction
An electric field E will induce and bind a charge q with the surface density

$$E = \frac{\sigma}{\varepsilon}$$

on a conductor placed in the field. If the conductor is grounded, a charge $-q$ will leak to ground. If the conductor is insulated the charge $-q$ will charge the conductor to a certain voltage, although the total charge on the conductor is zero. Electrostatic induction should not be mistaken for electromagnetic induction involving changing magnetic fields. *See also* **polarization**.

insulative material
Material with **surface resistivity** $\rho_s > 10^{12}$ Ω.

ion
See **air ion.**

ionization
When an electron is knocked off an oxygen or nitrogen molecule, an elementary positive ion is formed, which will attract 10–15 molecules (mostly water), forming a cluster called a positive air ion (or positive small ion). The electron attaches to an oxygen molecule, forming an elementary negative ion, which attracts maybe 8-12 water molecules, forming a negative ion (or small negative ion). Ions are always formed in pairs (positive/negative). Necessary energy to form an ion (about 34 eV or $5.4 \cdot 10^{-18}$ J) is delivered by radioactive radiation or by electrons accelerated in electric field. *See* **air ion**, and **ionizer**.

ionizer
Device to produce air ions.

Radioactive (nuclear) ionizer
Contains an α -active nuclide, often polonium (Po). Each α particle (energy $\sim 5 - 7$ MeV ($0.8 - 1 \cdot 10^{12}$ J)) produces 150,000–200,000 ion pairs along its range of 2–6 cm. *Advantage*: small dimensions and simple construction, no electrical circuits. No **ozone** production. **Electrical ionizer** produces ions by **corona discharge** from wire or point **emitters**. Can be driven by the charge on the object to be neutralized (**passive ionizer**) or at a few kV of AC or DC voltage. *Advantage*: Easy to regulate output.

machine model
See **ESD damage models.**

mobility
If a mobile charge carrier in an electric field **E** moves with a constant velocity v, the mobility k of the carrier is given by

$$v = k\mathbf{E}$$

Unit for mobility is $m^2 V^{-1} s^{-1}$. *See* **air ion**.

neutralization

Charges on negatively charged insulated conductors may be removed by grounding the conductor. Charges of positively charged insulated conductors and charges of both polarities on insulators cannot be removed, but the field from the charges can be neutralized by attracting oppositely charged carriers from the surrounding medium (e.g., ionized air or other conductive fluids) or from (semi-) conductive layers on the charged body itself. *See* **decay rate**.

nuclear ionizer

See **ionizer.**

ohm, Ω

Unit for electrical **resistance** and **surface resistivity**. Definition of 1 ohm is

$$1\,\Omega = 1\,\frac{\text{volt}}{\text{ampere}}$$

Ohm's law

If a material contains charge carriers with a charge q, concentration n, and **mobility** k, a field strength $\mathbf{E}$ will make the carriers move with a velocity $\mathbf{v}$ – $k\mathbf{E}$, causing a current density

$\mathbf{j}$ = $nq\mathbf{v} = nqk\mathbf{E} = \gamma\mathbf{E}$
γ = nqk is called the **bulk** or **volume conductivity** of the material. Unit is $\Omega^{-1} m^{-1}$
$\mathbf{j}$ = $\gamma\mathbf{E}$ is **Ohm's law** (in differential form). Often written $\mathbf{E} = \rho\mathbf{j}$, where

$$\rho = \frac{1}{\gamma}$$

ρ is called the **bulk** or **volume resistivity** of the material. Unit is Ωm.

If the current density is integrated over the whole current carrying area to give the current I and the field strength along the whole current path to yield the **voltage difference** V we get

$$I = GR \qquad \text{or} \qquad V = R1$$

where

$$R = \frac{1}{G}$$

This is **Ohm's law** (in integral form).

G is called the **conductance**. Unit is **siemens, Ω^{-1}**. R is the **resistance**. Unit is **ohm, Ω**. If a field strength $\mathbf{E}$, along a surface releases a current with the **linear current density** $\mathbf{j_s}$ $(A \cdot m^{-1})$ the **surface resistivity**, ρ_s of the material is defined by $\mathbf{E}_\phi = \rho_s \mathbf{j}_o$ which is **Ohm's law** for surface conduction. Unit for surface resistivity is

$$\frac{volt/meter}{ampere/meter} = \frac{volt}{ampere} = ohm, \ \Omega$$

and certainly *not* ohms per square.

ohm(s) per square (!)
Peculiar mixture of a unit and a geometric concept. Still sometimes (stubbornly) used in some countries instead of the proper unit for **surface resistivity**, which is ohm. *See* **Ohm's law**.

ozone, O_3
Chemically very active gas, formed at all types of electrical discharges. Production rate increases with corona current. Harmful to respiratory tract. Maximum permissible level (in many countries)-1 ppm.

passive ionizer
See **ionizer**.

permanent polarization
See **electret**.

permittivity
In vacuum, the relation between the dielectric displacement **D** and the corresponding electric field **E** is $\mathbf{D} = \varepsilon_o \mathbf{E}$, where $\varepsilon_o = 8.85 \ (4187818) \cdot 10^{-12} \ F \cdot m^{-1}$ is the **vacuum permittivity**. In a dielectric, the relation may be written $\mathbf{D} = \varepsilon \mathbf{E} = \varepsilon_t - \varepsilon_o \mathbf{E}$. ε is the **absolute permittivity** and ε_r the **relative permittivity** of the dielectric. For many common dielectrics, ε_r is about 2–6. If the field volume in a vacuum (or air) capacitor is filled with a dielectric, the capacitance becomes ε_r times greater. *See* **polarization**.

pink poly
See **antistatic agent**.

polarization
If a fixed charge creates an electric field E_o and dielectric displacement D_o in vacuum, and the field is filled with a dielectric, the dielectric displacement D remains unchanged equal to D_0 but the field E will be

$$E = \frac{1}{\varepsilon_r} E_0$$

This is caused by the formation of **dipoles** in the dielectric.

plateout
The deposition of airborne particulates by diffusion or aided by an electric field.

potential, potential difference
The potential is a property of a point in an electric field E. The **potential difference** between two points A and B in a field E is defined by

$$V_A - V_B - \int_A^B E \cdot da$$

The **potential** V_P of the point P is defined by

$$V_P = \int\limits_{P}^{\infty \text{ or ground}} E \cdot da$$

Unit for potential difference is volt where

$$1 \text{ volt} = 1 \frac{\text{joule}}{\text{coulomb}}$$

The potential of an insulated conductor G is

$$V_G = \int\limits_{G}^{\text{ground}} E \cdot da$$

with the same value for all points on or in the conductor.

The **surface potential**, V_S of a point S on the surface of any body is

$$V_S = \int\limits_{S}^{\text{ground}} E \cdot da$$

For insulators V_S will change from point to point and is therefore not suited to characterize the insulator (except for uniformly charged **electrets**).

precipitation
The removal from the air of solid or liquid particulates in an electric field. *See* **electrofilter**.

radioactive ionizer
See **ionizer.**

resistance
See **Ohm's law.**

resistivity
See **Ohm's law.**

separation
The separation by an electrical field of components of mixtures of materials with different electrical properties.

spark
Discharge between insulated, charged conductor, and ground or between two conductors at different **potentials** when neither conductor have sharp points or protrusions. If the capacitance of the charged conductor is C, the charge q, and voltage V, the energy

$$W = \frac{q^2}{2C} = \frac{1}{2} CV^2$$

may be dissipated in a discharge. The **spark discharge** is characterized by a narrow discharge path with high-energy density, which makes sparks the most incendive of all types of discharges.

spark discharge
  See **spark.**
static dissipative material
  Material with **surface resistivity** $\rho_s = 10^5 - 10^{12}\,\Omega$.
static electricity
  See **electrostatics.**
static eliminator
  See **ionizer.**
static material
  Old designation for material with **surface resistivity** $\rho_s > 10^{11}\Omega$.
static voltmeter
  See **electrometer.**
surface resistivity
  See **Ohm's law.**
surface potential
  See **potential.**
time constant
  See **decay rate.**
triboelectrification
  Charge separation between two materials caused by contact and friction. *See*
  triboelectric series.
triboelectric series
  List of materials arranged so that one material may be positively charged when
  rubbed against and separated from another material farther down the list.
  Almost a list of decreasing permittivity. Main use of list is to indicate polarities
  of charges separated and (with caution) to qualitatively estimate magnitude of
  charges based on interlist distance of materials.
volt
  Unit for **potential** and **potential difference** (**voltage** and **voltage difference**)

$$1 \text{ volt} = 1\,\frac{\text{joule}}{\text{coulomb}}$$

voltage
  See **potential.**
wrist strap
  Conductive bracelet connected to ground through resistor (1 MΩ) to secure
  person is at ground potential.

Index

About the author

Niels Jonassen received his M.S. from the University of Copenhagen in 1954 majoring in physics, and minoring in mathematics, chemistry and astronomy. In 1962 he received the Dr. Techn. (D.Sc.) degree from the Technical University of Denmark and in the same year the Danish Esso Prize for his work on industrial static electricity.

He has worked several periods in the United States (mostly New Mexico) on atmospheric electric and radioactive problems. He was a member of the OECD group of radon specialists, coauthoring the OECD report on Radon and Radon Daughters. He has twice been a UN specialist for the IAEA (International Atomic Energy Agency) to the Philippines, advising on radon projects.

Dr. Jonassen is a member of the ESD Association (and has served on its technical committee since 1985) and the Electrostatic Society of America. For 20 years he has been teaching a three-week full course on static electricity at the Technical University of Denmark and has been conducting about 70 extended courses on static electricity, ions, and indoor climate.

He received the ESD Association Outstanding Contribution Award in 1989. He has recently officially retired from the Technical University but is still running his office and laboratory.